THE EMMERDALE FARM BOOK OF COUNTRY LORE

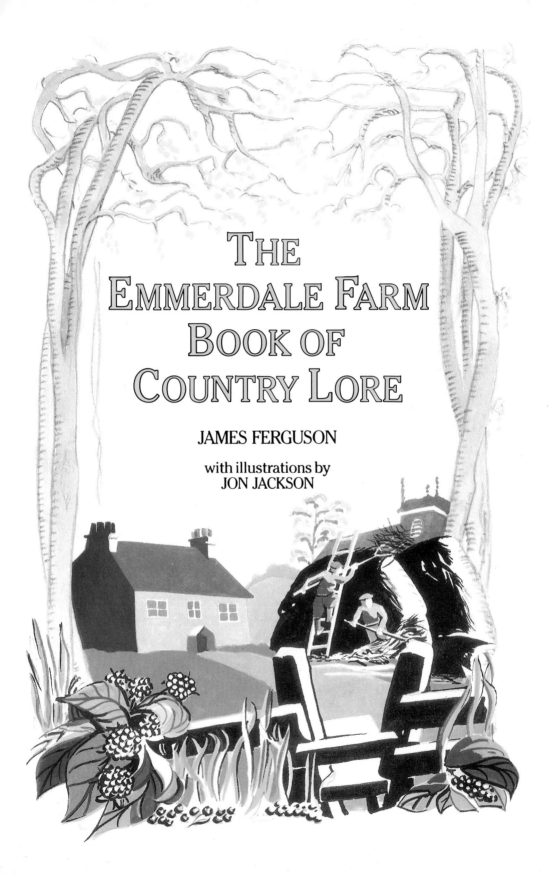

THE
EMMERDALE FARM
BOOK OF
COUNTRY LORE

JAMES FERGUSON

with illustrations by
JON JACKSON

First published 1988 by The Hamlyn
Publishing Group Limited, a division
of The Octopus Publishing Group,
Michelin House, 81 Fulham Road,
London SW3 6RB.

Text © copyright James Ferguson 1988

Photographs © ❤ Yorkshire Television Limited 1988

All photographs taken by Yorkshire Television Stills Dept.

Illustrations and design © copyright
The Hamlyn Publishing Group Limited 1988

ISBN 0 600 56012 0

Emmerdale and Emmerdale Farm are trade marks
of ❤ Yorkshire Television Limited

Printed in Shekou, China

CONTENTS

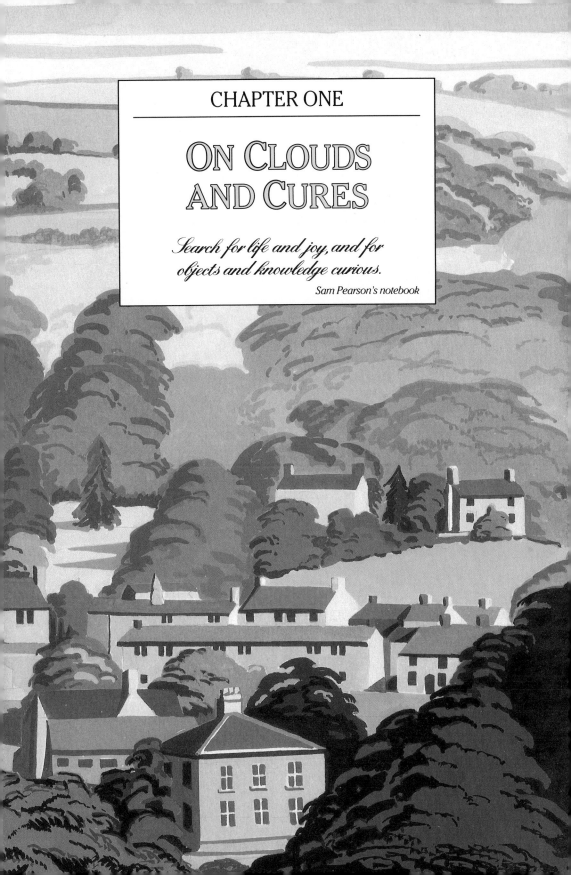

CHAPTER ONE

ON CLOUDS AND CURES

Search for life and joy, and for objects and knowledge curious.

Sam Pearson's notebook

I t was coffee time at Emmerdale Farm and the telephone was ringing as Jack walked into the empty kitchen. His hands were filthy from creosoting a fence and his first wish was to clean them at the sink, so he shouted for his mother.

'Ma, telephone!' There was no reply.

Looking at his brown-stained hands, he went across to the telephone and picked the handset up. 'Emmerdale,' he said, holding it gingerly to avoid covering it with the strong-smelling creosote.

'Jack?' It was his brother, Joe.

'Now then, Joe.' He used the Yorkshireman's greeting.

'I've been ringing for ages, where is everybody?' cried Joe. 'I thought some of you would have been in at 'lowance time.'

'I'm in,' laughed Jack. 'Dunno where Ma is. Anyroad, what's up? Is it urgent?'

'No, I just thought I'd get somebody if I rang now. But it's you I'm seeking, Jack. I've got summat for you, here at Demdyke.'

'Oh?' Jack was interested now. 'Summat nice, is it?'

'I dunno about that, it's a parcel.'

'Left by the postman, was it?'

'No, I've just found it. I'm clearing my attic and it was among some stuff Ma had stored here after Grandad died. It's among a lot of other odds and ends, a lot of it's junk to be honest, and I'm chucking most of it out, but this has got your name on, in Grandad's writing. It's tied up in brown paper with string round it.'

'That sounds interesting. What is it? Tools? Carvings of some kind? Summat he's made? From his workshop?'

'It feels like a book, Jack. Anyroad, I just wanted you to know it's here at Demdyke. Call in when you're passing. I'll leave it handy. I'll be here all day, just knock and walk in.'

'Aye, right. Thanks.'

Jack replaced the telephone, shouted again for Ma then began to scrub his hands. When they were reasonably clean, he put on the kettle and prepared to make his own coffee. Then Ma came in; she'd been to Matt and Dolly's.

'Oh, there you are, I thought you'd run off and left us,' grinned Jack.

'There's no reason why you shouldn't lend a hand with the coffee now and then!' she retorted. 'You can't expect me to be on hand every minute of the day. As it happens, I've been helping Dolly move a bed. Now you look after the coffee while I find some biscuits. Robert's round at Dolly's playing with some of young Sam's old toys and things.'

Jack smiled to himself as he prepared the coffee; today, there were only the two of them; Jackie and Kathy had gone to Hotten and Matt would go home for his break. Jack made two mugs full and placed them before his mother as she settled at the table for their 'lowance, as the mid-morning break was called.

'Take the one you want, Ma,' he laughed. 'They're top quality coffees, both of 'em. Now,' he continued, 'I've just had a call from Joe. He's found a parcel in his loft among some of Grandad's old stuff. He reckons it looks like a book or summat similar, and it's got my name on in Grandad's writing. Any idea what it could be?'

Annie's eyes lit up. 'Aye,' she said happily. 'Aye, I do know, but I'll let you find out for yourself. I wondered where that had got to ... I thought I'd accidentally thrown it out after Dad died. It's a relief to know I didn't!'

'Summat he left specially for me, is it?' Jack's curiosity was aroused.

'Aye,' she said. 'For you and mebbe for others ...'

'Right, I'll go for it now,' he said. 'That fence can wait! A few hours more without

Sam Pearson

protection won't hurt.'

Annie smiled with happiness as Jack drained his coffee and rushed off in the Land Rover. So Grandad's legacy had not been lost after all... in the months following his death, she'd searched high and low for this precious parcel.

She knew Grandad had nurtured it year after year, and for some time now, Annie had worried that it had been lost or thrown out inadvertently. She had never dared to tell the others that it was missing...and now Joe had rediscovered it. At last, Grandad's wishes would be fulfilled, for it would reach Jack's hands and Jack would know what to do with it.

GRANDAD'S LEGACY

Jack tapped on the door of Demdyke Cottage and shouted, 'Joe, you there?'

'Aye,' called a voice from the top of the stairs. 'Come in. It's on the kitchen table. Hang on before you open it, I want to see what it is. I like surprises.'

Jack went into the kitchen and saw the parcel. It was about twelve inches long by eight inches wide and three-quarters of an inch thick, neatly wrapped in stout brown paper and tied with a length of white string which was knotted in a loop. Jack noticed his own name printed in large letters on the wrapping. He picked it up and weighed it in his hands, feeling the dustiness of the covering and looking at the paper.

Then Joe came in, wiping his hands on a rag.

'There we are.' He beamed at the sight of the parcel in his brother's hand. 'The family heirloom, eh? The Sugden treasure. Well, aren't you going to open it?'

Jack nodded. 'Aye,' he said. 'It's a book, isn't it?'

'Could be,' grinned Joe. 'It's like Christmas all over again, or a birthday?'

Carefully, Jack loosened the knot and removed the string, then began to unwrap the brown paper. Inside, there was an old lined notebook; it had cheap board covers in a dark slate-blue colour with a fragile binding of red cloth-like material. It looked

Joe Sugden

to be of considerable age, probably thirty or forty years old, and it bore a faint smell of mustiness.

'So it is a book,' said Jack, opening it. 'It's like one of those thick exercise books that farmers used for keeping records. You remember, in most farmhouses, probably in the parlour, there would be an old desk, sometimes with a roll-top cover, and these thick books would be standing in a row, all labelled in black ink down their spines. There'd be some containing records of milking, others dealing with sheep production, the laying record of the hens and an egg tally, cattle movements and births of calves, horses and their shoeing and so on.'

Inside the front cover, Grandad's handwriting said, 'Sam Pearson's notebook' and, in the top left-hand corner, the original price was still visible, written in pencil. It said 1/9d and the pages were of lined paper, the faint blue lines being almost half an inch apart. It looked well handled and the corners of the pages were turned up through constant use.

'One shilling and ninepence,' said Jack. 'That's what it cost. That's just under 8p in today's money. So he bought it before decimalisation; that was in February 1971. I reckon he bought it a long time before 1971, judging by its appearance. With that price, I'd say he bought it in the 1950s.'

'When I was nobbut a lad!' smiled Joe. 'So what's in it?' He was keen to discover the secret of Grandad's notebook as Jack turned the first page. There was a short introductory note by Grandad:

'During my life, I learned a lot about country ways and about the animals, the weather, old traditions and so on. Over the years, I have recorded much of what I can remember, and this book is a collection of those memories. It is not complete – and never will be because time keeps moving – but I hope my grandchildren and others will find it both interesting and useful.'

The short note was signed, 'Sam Pearson.'

'He doesn't say what he wants you to do with it, does he?' Joe asked. 'In fact, the only reference to you is on the wrapping.'

'He'd leave it for me because I'm the eldest grandchild; you were in France, anyway, with no likelihood of returning, but he wouldn't expect to have to explain himself any more than that,' Jack said. 'So what am I to do with it?'

'Read it first, then decide,' said Joe. 'Come on, open up and let's see what he's been recording for posterity.'

Jack flicked through the pages, most of which were carefully compiled in Grandad's own handwriting, although there were a few newspaper cuttings and one or two notes from other people whom Sam had obviously approached for a note of their own recollections.

'It's got all sorts, Joe.' Although Jack had

rapidly scanned the pages, he had seen enough to appreciate the breadth of its contents. 'Pig-killing days, strawberries, why we spit on our hands before doing an important job, weather sayings, all sorts of scraps about wildlife, birds, animals, insects, flowers, trees...old sayings, dialect words, customs...'

'It must have taken him years to compile that,' Joe said.

'Aye, and he must have a keen eye to notice things himself, things that were happening around him as the months and years went by. Listen, there's a section on clouds,' Jack added. 'I'll read it out to you. I never thought Grandad knew so much about clouds!'

CLOUDS

Jack settled at Joe's kitchen table to read and Joe relaxed before him.

Joe said. 'I remember when I was a lad, Grandad would point to any clouds that appeared on a fine morning and he'd say it generally meant a fine evening. Another thing he told me was that if the clouds were going across the wind a storm could be expected and if they floated at different heights and at different speeds, usually in opposing directions, then heavy rain was likely.'

'He's got a note about that,' Jack said. 'These are the sort of things most folks hear about but seldom put on record.'

'Does he name the clouds?' Joe asked. 'I remember at school we did a project about the weather, and we had to learn the names of clouds. I can still recall them after all these years – there were three main types, cirrus, cumulus and stratus, each with sub-divisions.'

'They taught us all sorts in those days,' Jack recalled.

'Aye,' agreed Joe. 'And the sub-divisions of the cirrus are cirrostratus which made the sky look watery and created rings around the sun or moon, and the cirrocumulus which causes what we call a mackerel sky. That's when small groups of clouds appear high in the sky during a fine spell and it's a sure sign that rain or unsettled weather is coming, but it also means it won't be unsettled for long.'

Jack laughed. 'There's quite a few notes in Grandad's book about the mackerel sky.' He flipped through the pages. 'Listen:

Mackerel sky and mares' tails
Make lofty ships carry low sails.'

'Mares' tails are cirrus clouds which are very thin, almost clear and they stretch in thin lines across the sky; they seem to appear when the weather is about to change,' said Joe. 'I remember that, an' all!'

Jack went on, 'There's more verses about a mackerel sky:

Mackerel sky, mackerel sky
Never long wet and never long dry.

A mackerel sky, not twenty-four hours dry

Mackerel scales, furl your sails.'

'Right, has he written anything about the other clouds, Jack?'

'Grandad says here that cumulus clouds are called rainballs in Lancashire, but I'm not sure whether Yorkshire folk would agree with anything a Lancastrian says!' grinned Jack. 'He does mention those that look like castles and says that when large, irregular masses of cloud look like rocks, towers or turrets, then showers are forecast, with probably longer periods of rain as well. He's got some more verses here:

A round topped cloud with flattened base
Carries rainfall in its face.

When clouds appear like rocks and towers

The earth's refreshed by frequent showers.

'And,' continued Jack. 'He says that some rounded clouds are called water-wagons because they carry so much rain.'

'One of Grandad's favourites was Barbara and her bairns,' Joe recalled. 'That was a whopping big cloud that appeared on the horizon and it was surrounded by lots of little ones. It was like a mother hen and her chicks, or a woman and her children, but she must has been a rough one because when Barbara and her bairns appeared, it meant stormy weather.'

'That could be a stratocumulus, one of the stratus family of clouds,' Jack now aired his knowledge.

'Now here's a piece I didn't know,' he went on. 'Small clouds on hills used to be called fops here in the north.'

'Fops?' puzzled Joe. 'I've never heard that before.'

'Me neither, but that's one of his notes. He's got a saying here which goes:

When it gangs up i' fops
It'll come down in drops.'

'What's that mean?' asked Joe.

'I think it means that if small clouds gather on the hill tops, then it will rain before long.'

'He's included a lot about the weather then?' Joe put to him.

'It seems full of it, but it is important to a farmer and a countryman. Joe. Our livelihood depends on the weather and in this country, that means we have a very uncertain existence! Looking at it logically, there's little wonder that folks like our Grandad and those before him learned to forecast it.'

'Aye, we've come to rely on the Met. Office and its forecasts on radio and TV; in spite of all their up-to-date equipment and their computers, they don't seem to make a better job of it than Grandad and his forefathers. Now, I fancy a coffee and I'm going to make this an official break during my cleaning session. Fancy one?'

'I had one at Emmerdale before I came here,' Jack said.

'That doesn't stop you having another.'

'Go on then,' smiled Jack. 'I'll see what else is in here while you're brewing up.'

FIRST AID

Joe returned with the coffees and Jack said, 'You know, Joe, this is full of good stuff. He's chatted to folks in Beckindale too, and he's picked their brains about all manner of country ways. Actually, it might not be just country ways, because he's included a fair bit of household superstition and custom, things that I suppose some townsfolk do.'

'Such as?' Joe settled down opposite his brother and sipped the coffee.

'Well, listen to this. Do you know you can use a raw potato for first aid purposes?'

'Really? How?'

'One simple way is for curing headaches. You cut a raw potato into thin slices and simply press one or more of them on the forehead. Some say it eases migraine too.'

'That reminds me of when I was working in France,' Joe said. 'One of our office girls spilt some boiling water over her hand and, without hesitating, another girl rushed into the kitchen at our estate office and brought back a raw potato. She cut it into slices and pressed one or two of them against the scald marks. It certainly eased the pain, and there were no marks left afterwards. I would have forgotten that if you hadn't mentioned potato aid!'

'Grandad mentions somewhere in here that they were used to cure rheumatism and all manner of rashes and pains or burns and scalds. In these cases, the raw potato was sliced and placed directly upon the skin.'

'Do these things actually work?' asked Joe. 'It's all right Grandad claiming they do, but has anybody ever tested them?'

'The answer is for us to test them whenever it becomes necessary, Joe. This is just country lore, you know, not a book of medical treatments! But you saw it work in France!'

'Aye, and my response would be that the French girl might have been okay without that treatment; in other words, she might not have been too severely hurt.'

'Well, Joe, these things have been well tested and tried down the years, so it's up to

individuals to decide whether they're genuine or not.'

'Do you remember when we were lads? If we got stung by nettles when we were playing, Ma would spit on a docken leaf and cover our stung parts with it. It seemed to work. She once used a bruised onion when I got stung by a wasp,' Joe went on. 'And I once remember Grandad talking about poultices, I've never come across one being used on humans, but they do use 'em to draw infections from horses' hooves.'

'He's mentioned them here, Joe. You're too young to remember Ma using them, but I can – just. I was once smothered in a bread poultice when I had a chest infection.'

'So what is a poultice?' asked Joe.

'I'll see what Grandad says,' and Jack spent a few minutes turning the pages until he found an entry on poultices. 'Here we are. Poultices were made with various ingredients mixed with boiling water and spread on a piece of muslin or other cloth, and then applied to a part of the body which required treatment. They were applied when still hot. The idea was that the heat from the poultice, and its special ingredients, would draw off the injurious matter or pain.'

'What was in them?' asked Joe.

'There's a list here in Grandad's notebook,' said Jack. 'I don't think it's complete, but it'll give you some idea. Right, there was bread poultice, this was used to draw the matter out of boils and other inflamed parts or even bruises. It would even help to ease scratches made by briars or a cat! A potato poultice was reckoned to be good for easing burns, scalds, boils and abscesses of various kinds as well as general soreness, while a hot onion poultice was recommended for boils. In applying these, by the way, they had not to be too hot, otherwise they might blister a tender part! Some poultices were used for easing rheumatism, such as honey and nettle poultice, fig or slippery elm poultice, while a caraway seed poultice was useful in easing earache if it was applied to the outside of the ear. Several of these were also useful for easing abrasions, cuts and bruises.'

'It used to be said that wounds could be made to stop bleeding by applying a spider's web,' said Joe. 'I once read that somewhere.'

'It's here,' grinned Jack. 'You simply gather a handful of spiders' webs and roll them into a ball or pat them into a flat pad. Then you cover the wound with them. They make a very effective seal and have been used for centuries for this purpose. The Marquess of Worcester recommended it in 1665.'

'Did you know,' Joe winked cheekily at his brother, 'that the web of a spider is the strongest and lightest material known on earth? It is stronger than drawn steel of the same diameter, so scientists would have us believe.'

'Go on, astound me!' said Jack teasingly. 'What else can you tell me about them?'

'Well, it's said that a half pound ball of spider's web would stretch around the world. It's produced instantly, as you'll see if a spider falls from a height, and a spider is capable of producing endless lengths of it. And some spiders use their webs as means of transport, spinning them from a high place and waiting for a passing breeze to catch them. As the web is borne off by the wind, the spider hangs on to the end and flies off, sometimes travelling up to 40 miles at heights ranging up to 10,000 feet.'

'And they usually seem to descend across our front door,' laughed Jack. 'Have you ever gone out at night and walked straight into a length of web strung across the path?'

'Now you know where they come from,' smiled Joe. 'Actually, the little fellow at the end of one of those webs is probably some youthful spider who has just left mother's nest; if he doesn't leave at the right time she'll eat him, so this is one way of avoiding the risk of being mum's dinner.'

'I like the country name for those circular webs that become so noticeable in the dew on shrubs and hedgerows in the autumn,' said Jack. 'Gossamers, we call them. It's a lovely name, very descriptive.' He paused for a moment to reflect upon them, and then drained his coffee. 'Well, Joe, I can't sit around all day when there's fences to be creosoted. I must be off.'

'What are you going to do with this book, then?' asked Joe.

'I'll read it first, then see if it's complete. There might be items to add and there'll be a

spot of editing to do, getting those loose sheets and newspaper clippings into the right place.'

'Do you reckon Grandad wanted you to publish it? I mean, you are a published writer as well as being his eldest grandson, so he clearly wants you to make a decision.'

'I'll think about it,' said Jack, preparing to leave.

'Can you leave it here for me to have another look at?' requested Joe. 'I'm coming up to Emmerdale for supper tonight, so I'll bring it with me.'

'Sure,' agreed Jack. 'Let me know what you think of it.'

And he left Demdyke Cottage.

POT-POURRI

Joe made himself another coffee as he settled in an easy chair to dip into his grandfather's notebook. He did not read it from cover to cover, but found himself opening it at random to find a wealth of miscellaneous subjects. One of the first was pot-pourri. His grandfather had made a note to say that someone had asked Annie how to make pot-pourri and she had provided the answer. That answer was now part of his book. Annie had told Grandad:

'You will require a lot of patience because making pot-pourri is a long job. You will have to gather rose petals and other flowers and leaves which have a strong scent. You could include rosemary, geranium leaves, lavender, thyme or anything which has a pleasing but powerful scent.

'Many of these can be found in our own garden, but friends will always supply extra ingredients – often in return for a share of the finished product!

'When you have gathered together your flowers, herbs and leaves, spread them on a tray covered with a sheet of newspaper and let them dry naturally in the sunshine. A quiet and sunny windowledge indoors is the ideal place.

'This drying will take about a fortnight and it is important that each item is completely dry. Make sure every piece can gain the utmost benefit from the sunshine. If there is any dampness left in any one of them it will cause all the other pieces to go rotten, so the importance of this early part of the process cannot be stressed too highly.

'When these are thoroughly dry they can then be placed in a large mixing bowl for the next stage.

'It is now that other ingredients can be added. These may include: bay salt, powdered nutmeg, cinnamon, cloves, orris root and various flower oils – these can be obtained from suppliers such as chemists or herbalists. Some recipes include oil of lavender and sweet geranium, a very small amount of the strong oil of bergamot, oil of sweet orange and rose water.

'The rind of a lemon, thinly sliced, can also be added, as well as allspice and flowered benzoin, which is a very fragrant resin. Try some other recipes and don't be afraid of suggesting additional ingredients to make your own brand of pot-pourri.

'When these have been thoroughly mixed, preferably by stirring gently with your hand, the entire contents of the bowl should then be placed in a large sealed container which is airtight. They should then be allowed to settle. It is wise to gently shake the container every two days or so and, if necessary, further petals and herbs can be added provided they have gone through that vital drying process.

'Leave the container for at least a month or even two months, regularly shaking the contents, and after this time it should be ready for use. Place the pot-pourri in small muslin bags or sachets – these can be hung in wardrobes or placed in drawers among clothing – or put it in small finger bowls or even in a pomander, which is a container made specially for the purpose. If the pot-pourri is in an open bowl the scent may weaken as it settles down, but it can be quickly revived simply by stirring with a finger. The perfume will remain for a long, long time and it will remind you of the glories of summer.'

Joe chuckled as he then read of an old custom at York Assizes where the judge was presented with a casket of sweet herbs to take with him into the court room. Certainly, the prisoners and probably the rooms within York Assizes in bygone times would have benefited from this thoughtful gift!

He recalled that he had often seen pot-pourri in small glass dishes around the house at Emmerdale and had wondered how it had been produced. Now he made a note to remind his mother to make some for his new premises at Home Farm.

THE GATEPOST BARGAIN

One of the shorter notes written by Grandad went: 'In my day, and indeed well into this century, many of the farmers of the Yorkshire Dales lived in very remote places. The farmhouses were usually at the end of a long, rough track and this made it difficult and time-consuming for regular tradesmen to call.

'People like the postman, the newspaper lad, the butcher or the bread man and others who made regular calls would leave their deliveries on the gatepost at the farm entrance, and we would collect them when we had time. This also applied to paying money out; when the insurance man called, he would find his money on the gatepost.

'The farmer's wife would leave her cash out for regular callers of the kind I've mentioned. Nobody ever stole the money and everyone behaved like this.

'This also applied to the sale of cattle or sheep in the fields. The buyer would purchase the animals as they stood in the field, but they had to pay before the animals could be removed. They did this by leaving the money on the gatepost; once the money was on the gatepost, the deal was concluded and the cattle could be removed. This became known as a "gatepost bargain".

'This is similar to the saying of "paying on the nail". This means paying on the spot or settling up immediately, and the saying probably originated from the habit of leaving the cash payments in special receptacles called nails. These were mounted on stands in markets and corn exchanges. It was really a type of flat or very shallow dish, and the name might have come from the combined shape of the dish and the post upon which they were mounted. They did look like giant nails and you can still see examples outside the Corn Exchange in Bristol.

'On the subject of deals involving livestock, when a farmer has done a deal in the cattle mart or elsewhere, he will confirm it by slapping the hand of the other person involved, sometimes calling "Done"; then, when the payment is made, the buyer will hand back a small sum as luck money. There seems to be no set amount or percentage for this luck money.

'It might be a pound or even a five pound note these days, or even more depending upon the size of the transaction, but it is a very essential part of any deal. It is considered offensive not to give luck money at the conclusion of a successful deal.'

Later that evening, Joe took Grandad's notebook back to Emmerdale Farm and was greeted by Annie.

'Jack's popped out to see Henry at the Woolpack,' she told him. 'He said you'd found Grandad's notebook?'

Joe showed his mother the old notebook, told her of his discovery and praised the foresight of his grandfather in placing his memories on record.

'You knew he was keeping this record, didn't you, Ma?' Joe smiled.

'I did. He kept it very secret for a long time, then as he got nearer the end of his life, I think he knew he had to include as much as possible. So he began to ask questions around the place, filling that old book with his observations. I'm so glad it's been found, Joe. I thought it had been lost for ever.'

'There's nothing from Grandad to say what he wants us to do with it? My own opinion is that it's great and we should try to get it in print somehow.'

'You remember how quiet and reserved your Grandad was; he was far too shy to think of getting it published himself, but I think he thought Jack might look at it and decide what to do. Mebbe you could make sure he reads it and does what he thinks is best?'

'Aye,' said Joe. 'I will.'

CHAPTER TWO

ON FARM
AND FIELD

A man should live within his harvest.

Sam Pearson's notebook

T he more Jack examined his grandfather's notebook, the more he realised it contained a veritable treasury of farming, gardening and country lore. Most of it was maintained in Sam Pearson's distinctive handwriting. There were old sayings which Sam had collected, details of weather lore, advice on planting seeds and harvesting, old superstitions and customs, an assortment of the lore on wild life and samples of Yorkshire dialect words. Grandad had written notes in the fear that some aspects of rural life might become obsolete.

As he glanced through the pages, Jack recalled his grandfather's annual ritual of looking at the weather on Easter Sunday and then saying, 'Well, Jack, whatever the weather today, it'll be the same at harvest time. It's funny how that happens, you know, but it does. You mark my words. And I'll tell you summat else, Jack Sugden, one day you'll notice these things like I do and you'll know they make sense.'

Jack smiled with pleasure at this reminder of Grandad's rural wisdom and settled down to read the notes. Under the heading 'Planting Time', he found a short diary entry which served as a reminder for the times Sam had to plant his garden – and there were brief jottings on caring for it in the hope that his vegetables would beat those of Seth Armstrong and Amos Brearly at the Beckindale Horticultural Society's annual show!

ON PLANTING

Grandad's notes said: 'Always plant plenty – remember

One for the rook, one for the crow
One to die and one to grow.

Start gardening with pride
On the feast of St Bride.

'St Bride's Day is February 1st and many people start gardening about now, or on Candlemas Day.'

A few days later, as Jack settled down in the parlour to read the notes, Joe came in bearing two mugs of coffee.

'Ma said you were in here.' Joe handed one of the mugs to his elder brother, then settled in an easy chair. 'Still reading Grandad's notes?'

Jack said he was enjoying them and that he was now reading Sam's notes about gardening.

Joe smiled. 'I remember him saying "When the beans are in flower, fools are in power" and he evidently thought beans were a problem because he used to quote several verses about planting them. I remember him saying "On Candlemas Day, stick beans in the clay" or "Sow beans in Candlemas waddle". Another of his beliefs was "Beans should be in the clay by St Valentine's Day" and he always said "On St Valentine's Day, set thy hopper by mine". That means all planting should be under serious consideration by then.'

Jack felt happy at Joe's recollections, and added, 'He used to lecture me about gardening. He tried to make me as keen as he was, but it never worked! Mind, I can remember some of his sayings – those he's included in these notes – such as stressing that St Valentine's Day was a good day for sowing all manner of garden seeds, especially peas, lettuce, cabbages and even sweet peas. If it fell on a Sunday, he said you had to make sure nobody caught you working – he told me he used to get up very early to do his Sunday planting in secret if it fell on Valentine's Day. Up in Scotland, they don't plant their peas until the swallows arrive and in some parts of England, they look out for the arrival of the yellow wagtail before planting – it usually gets here in mid-April. Now, another of his sayings was "On St Matthias' day, take thy hopper and sow" (St Matthias' Day is February 24th), and he'd say, "Sow

Jack Sugden

peas and beans on Saints David and Chad, whether the weather be good or bad"; and "On St David's Day, put oats and barley in the clay".'

Joe nodded. 'Aye, and round here, they still follow those guidelines. St David's Day is March 1st and St Chad's is March 2nd. Chad was Abbot of Lastingham in North Yorkshire, and his brother, St Cedd, is buried there. They reckoned that every goose laid an egg on St Chad's day, and daffodils bloom on St David's Day. In some parts of Yorkshire, they plant onions on St Gregory's Day, that's March 21st; because he was Pope Gregory the Great, they seem to think they'll get great onions! It's Farmers' Day on March 21st, an' all!'

Jack read aloud from Grandad's notes. 'He's got a strange note here that says "Be it weal or be it woe, beans should blow before May go". I think this means beans should be showing above the ground before the end of May, or it might be before the blackthorn or the hawthorn blossom disappears. They are

both called may or may blossom by country folk.'

Joe interrupted him. 'Still on about beans, I've heard Grandad say that kidney beans should be planted before the leaves of the trees unfurl, and if they're going to produce plenty of beans, they've got to be planted before the elm leaves are as big as a florin, that's a 10p piece these days. He said broad beans should be sown on St Thomas' Day, which is December 21st, and one funny notion he had was that during a leap year all beans should be planted upside down – and he swore that beans grew backwards in their pods during a leap year! Another thing he once told me was that in parts of Yorkshire, beans were sometimes given out at funerals as the children shouted "God save your soul, beans and all".'

Jack knew that his grandfather placed some importance on these rural beliefs and read further extracts from the notes. He said, 'Grandad's got here that onions and shallots must be planted on St Thomas' Day, the idea being that to plant on the shortest day of the year would enable a good crop to be gathered on the longest day, that's June 21st. Some say the best day for planting shallots is Christmas Day.'

Joe had heard old Sam say the same thing. 'He always told me that cabbages are best planted around New Year, and that a covering of snow was good for all seeds. He said it was the poor man's fertiliser, and if it fell after the onions had been planted, he called it an "onion snow".'

'St Patrick's Day is next.' Jack was turning the pages. 'That's when sweet peas should be sown, and it's when they plant their potatoes in Ireland. The Americans plant their cabbages on this day too, and the Irish wear shamrocks! Now, he's got a note here that says "Never plant on the blind days".'

'What are those?' asked Joe.

'He's got a note explaining them,' Jack said. 'They're the first three days of April and Grandad says seeds planted during those days will never survive. He says we should keep away from the Borrowing Days as well; they're the last three days of March which are borrowed from April, as in this verse:

> March borrowed from April
> Three days and they were ill;
> The first o' them was wind and weet
> The second full o' snow and sleet;
> The third o' them was sike a freeze
> That the birds' feet stuck to the trees.'

'He once told me it wasn't a good idea to plant on the first three days of May either,' Joe said. 'Do it when the mulberry leaves are out, he'd say, then there'll be no more frosts. That's quite a good guide for delicate plants.'

ON POTATOES

Jack now drained his coffee and chuckled at the memories evoked by the next section of Grandad's notes. They bore the heading 'Potatoes', and read:

'I'm oft asked when's the best time to plant potatoes. Some say it's when the yellow wagtail arrives around the middle of April and I've heard this bird called the potato-setter because gardeners and farmers would watch for it before planting taties. Others say it's best to wait for the cuckoo; he comes in the middle of April as well, but some gardeners wait till he sings before planting their French beans and taties. "When you first hear the cuckoo shout, it's time to plant your taties out." Now, Good Friday is *the* day for planting potatoes. Out at Bridlington and on the coast, some like to plant them when the tide is rising, and it's reckoned best to plant them when the moon is coming up to full if this is possible. It makes them grow better. I've noticed this often happens on Good Friday, because the date of Easter is determined by the phases of the moon.

'Some reckon it's best to go to church before planting, but the old men say the devil has no dominion over the soil on Good Friday. It's by far the best time to start your gardening year.

'Some folk always carry a potato in their pockets because they think it cures rheumatism; it is best if it's a new one, and it can be kept for years until it's rock hard.'

The notes continued, 'Some would rub warts with a cut potato to cure them, and put the tatie in the ground thinking that when it rotted it would take away the wart.

'One thing I like to grow near my taties is a clump of foxgloves; they help to keep potatoes clear of diseases and make them better to keep when we store them. Another idea is to put grass cuttings in the holes and set each tatie on top of them. That keeps diseases away. It's said that "Plant your taties when you will, they'll not come up before April". But when we dig up the first roots of new potatoes, everybody in the family has to taste them at dinner. This ensures that the rest of the crop will be a good one, and we always make sure we make a wish when we bite into the first one!'

ON PARSLEY

As the brothers savoured their memories of Grandad Pearson, Jack offered Joe a glass of fine malt whisky, and he accepted. Jack poured himself a measure too.

'Thanks, Jack. Cheers – here's to absent friends,' and they toasted Grandad's memory. Joe continued, 'Parsley was one of his favourites, Jack. Has he mentioned that?'

'He has,' Jack said. 'Listen. I'll read what he says:

'"Parsley. Parsley should be planted on Good Friday and it will never grow in a garden where the wife is boss of the household! For seven times, it seeks the Devil before starting to grow, and it must be planted by an honest man. If a woman plants parsley, she'll soon become pregnant!

'"One old lady I knew said parsley was good for men wanting to become fathers because it made them stronger in that department – it was an aphrodisiac. Some girls would eat parsley to get rid of unborn babies, but I don't know if that ever worked! I've even heard that baby girls were found under parsley plants while little boys were found under gooseberry bushes.

'"But parsley is good for roses, because it makes them smell better, and they reckon it helps keep the greenfly off. It makes sense to grow it near turnips, carrots, beans and asparagus, because it makes them healthy too.

'"There is a saying that 'A parsley field will bring a man to his saddle and a woman to her grave' and you should never give away a parsley root; it brings bad luck.

'"I've seen my dear departed wife and our Annie garnish dishes with parsley. It's very healthy, but garnishing's been done for centuries and it comes from the days when parsley was considered an antidote to some poisons. And it was good for sheep – we'd let ours graze on the parsley beds to keep them healthy, and some farmers would chew it themselves to ease their rheumatics."'

HARVEST

'You know, Jack,' Joe said, 'our Grandad was typical of a Dalesman. He worried about planting his crops and the moment that was done, he started worrying about harvesting.'

Jack agreed. 'He's got a stack of notes about harvest. But let's be right about it – it was, and still is, such a vital part of a farmer's life. This is what he says:

'"A successful harvest is so important and I believe that 'The farmer's year starts after harvest'. I'm a big believer that anybody who has a good harvest must always expect a few thistles among it, and there is a saying that 'Harvest doesn't come every day, but it does come every year'. Those are wise sayings, and so is 'Short harvests make short addlins'. The word 'addlins' means earnings or wages, and around the Dales, the country folk spoke of hard addlins or poor addlins, and often said that 'Saving money is good addlins'."'

Jack brooded a moment on the deeper meanings contained in those words, then continued to read aloud.

'"If the north wind blows in June, it means a good harvest of grain, while a dripping June brings all in tune and a wet June often means a dry September. And that's good for harvesting! I always reckon that if the bramble blossoms early in June, you can expect a good harvest, especially here in Yorkshire. You can never be certain, though, because crops in other folks' fields always seem better than your own and that's unsettling. They say you'll never get good corn from a bad field, but a little field can grow big crops!

'"I happen to know that some big fields

grow poor crops and I also know that a harvest depends more on the year than on the field. And remember, you can tell the condition of a whole sackful of grain by just one handful from it!"'

At this point, Jack laughed at a note in the margin which said, 'Remind our vicar to ring the church bells before harvest – that's to make sure it's a good harvest.' Another similar note said, 'Stooks of corn should stand in the fields while the church bells ring twice – that makes sure they dry properly for about two weeks.'

'This next bit is a slice of farming history,' Jack told Joe. 'Listen, it's all about harvesting by hand. This is what he says: "When the corn was cut, it was made into stooks and these stood in the field. A stook comprised twelve shaffs of cut corn, and the stooks were set up in the field so that the weather and the wind would dry them. It was important that there was a hole in the bottom so

that air would enter and circulate. A shaff was a sheaf of cut corn, about a good armful, and this was tied in the middle. It stood as part of a stook with the grain heads uppermost. Teams of about ten men were involved in cutting and stooking the corn by hand; the cutters used either sickles or scythes (lyes), the sharpener being called a strickle. A team might be three scythers, three liers-out who laid out the cut corn, three scrampers who tied it into shaffs, and one to stook it.

'"When the corn was dry it was carted to the barn for storage, there to be threshed at a later stage. There was a small doorway in most barns through which individual shaffs could be passed, and we called this the shaff-hole. Threshing was a busy time. For centuries this was done by flails and these were in use in some hill farms on the Yorkshire moors until the 1930s; in fact, even into the late 1960s, some hill farmers in the remoter parts were still using flails to thresh

their very small crops.

'"A flail was sometimes called a stick and a half because it was made from two lengths of wood. One was the handstaff, which was about 4ft 6 inches long and usually made from willow or ash, and the other was the swipple, made from a thicker length of hazel or holly about 2ft 6 inches long. They were linked by a cleverly arranged ring so that the swipple could be swung around at the end of the handstaff and then brought heavily down upon the shaff of corn to loosen the grains. Men were hired to thresh by the threave (a threave was two stooks or twenty-four shaffs), and they undertook to thresh a specific number each day. If two men worked in unison they had to create an even working rhythm, sometimes described as 'tip, tap, top, like a clock ticking'. It required great skill, especially when operating in large groups. The shaff was first threshed on one side and then turned over for a repeat on the other side. Some of the small farmers would thresh just enough for one day's use at a time, for making flour or for feeding the livestock.

'"In all cases, the pile of corn that resulted was taken away for storage and the straw was stacked away for later use as animal bedding. The surplus chaff was removed by windering, sometimes called winnowing. This could be done by opening all the doors of a barn so that there was a through draught. This blew away all the surplus bits of straw and the husks – chaff as we called it, or just caff. Other times, the corn was passed through a riddle so that it fell into a heap or a sack as the chaff (caff) collected on the mesh. Caff-riddling, as we called it. Another way was to let the mixture of chaff and corn fall to the ground from a high balcony in the barn; the corn fell straight down as the chaff floated off. As we say in Yorkshire, there's no corn without caff, but we know that a lot of

first-class corn can lie under a covering of rubbishy caff. And remember this: 'You can't catch old birds with caff!'

'"Gradually, around the turn of the century, machines took over threshing, at first being operated by horses, then by steam and later by internal combustion engines. Teams of men came to help out on threshing days, but the combine harvester put an end to all that hard work – and happiness."'

THE HARVEST MOON

'How about that?' beamed Jack. 'Nostalgia unlimited! Those were the days, Joe.'

'I'll admit there was pride in getting the harvest gathered in, but it was really hard work,' said Joe.

'Think of the job satisfaction though!' Jack said. 'Anyway, he's continued his notes with the harvest moon. This is what he says:

'"You've got to bear in mind that the weather changes with the moon. Generally, there's a full moon around harvest time and that gives us more light to work by as we work late to gather it in. My own dad used to reckon that a Harvest Moon hanging high in the sky meant dear bread that year, in other words, that a poor harvest was due. But it's always said that gathering fruit of any sort while the moon is on the wane means the fruit will last a long time. It's different when it comes to planting. You should never plant seeds or transplant plants when the moon is waning, except beans and peas because they climb their supports anti-clockwise; seeds are best sown when the moon is waxing for it makes them grow better.

'"Again, my old dad never liked any of his harvested crops or fruit to lie for any length of time in moonlight; he used to say this rotted them. He would say potatoes and even grain would rot if the moon's rays got to them. Even so, he said it was a good idea to dig up potatoes when the moon was full. He said this would make the crop bigger and better. He would look at the moon every Christmas because he said that if Christmas was bright with moonlight, then the next harvest would not be a very good one because the yield would be light. But if Christmas didn't have a moon and was dark, then we'd have a good, heavy crop next harvest time."'

CORN DOLLIES

The brothers sat in silence for a moment or two, savouring the malt whisky, then Joe

said, 'Just before I went to France, Grandad told me about the old mell suppers and corn dollies. He was a bit concerned that we didn't have mell suppers like the old days, but I said we didn't have the same volume of workers helping with the harvest. Even so, Grandad thought a mell supper might be a good idea for Emmerdale. And even I can remember seeing corn dollies that were made after harvest – some were in the churches and chapels of the Dales and now you can buy poor examples in souvenir shops and on market stalls!'

'The corn dollies came about from the superstitions surrounding the cutting of the last sheaf,' said Jack.

'Aye, Grandad told me,' Joe continued. 'It seems there was always a bit of a fuss about that. Years ago, farmers thought it was unlucky to be the one who actually cut the last sheaf, so they'd race each other to make sure their workers didn't cut the last one in their village or dale. When enough corn was left in a field to make a sheaf, the workers would tie the stems in a bunch where it stood, then throw sickles at it. The idea was to cut it down without the sickle actually being held by anyone.

'In some Yorkshire dales, the workers would go to the lengths of paying somebody else to cut the last one so that the bad luck was spread about as many people as possible, and so weakened. Only when the bad luck had been cast away was that last sheaf cut, and then it was skilfully fashioned into something resembling a human figure. This was done by plaiting the straw and tying it in the middle to form a rough head and waist.'

'Now,' added Jack. 'I can go further back than that! The figure was always dressed like a girl doll, in female clothes with lots of ribbons. This corn dolly, kern baby or corn maiden as it was sometimes called, was also known as the mell sheaf. In some cases, these dollies were beautifully crafted as spirals or globes of plaited corn, and some were even made into the shape of miniature stacks of corn and used in the church at harvest festivals. But whatever their shape, they were known as corn dollies.

'So,' Jack continued. 'When the dolly was made, there was a celebration. Mell cakes – small buns like scones – were brought into the fields with drinks and sometimes fruit. It was a picnic with races, singing, contests, dancing and even half a day's holiday if the work was finished early enough. Sometimes this party was held inside the farmhouse, when it was called the kern supper.

'A kern supper occurred when the last sheaf was cut and usually consisted of the farm hands and family; the mell supper was given when the entire harvest was over and was a much bigger affair, with all the neighbours invited and, in fact, most of the village. Nowadays, some villages hold a mell supper in the parish halls after their harvest festival. But a kern supper was good fun and the corn dolly would be brought into the house where she was kept right through until the next harvest. Her presence brought good fortune.'

'Aye, I remember seeing a corn dolly at Emmerdale sometimes, when I was a lad,' said Joe. 'Grandad once told me that, in the old Yorkshire days, when the last shaff was cut, one of the workers would climb into a cart or on to a high wall, and shout:

Blest be the day when Christ was born
We've getten t'Mell of t'Sugden corn,
It's weel bun and better shorn,
Hurrah, hurrah, hurrah.'

'I've never come across that,' Jack admitted. 'But the odd thing is that some of our harvest customs go back to classical times and involve Ceres, the goddess of the harvest. She was said to be present in every harvest as the corn spirit. It was Ceres (who gives us our word cereal) who concealed the corn seed in the earth and whose generosity brought it forth as corn.'

Jack paused to fill his glass, then continued, 'I wonder how many Yorkshire farmers realise they are still honouring a pagan Roman goddess as they celebrate with their corn dollies? Some call them dozzles, by the way, and some make small dozzles to decorate their corn stacks after harvest. Over near Bridlington (once known as Burlington) where Matt and Dolly go for their holidays, the harvest workers used to "burn the old witch". When the final shaff was cut, they'd make a fire of the stubble, peas would be cooked in the heat and they'd make merry with lots of beer, fiddle-playing, dancing and singing. Any peas that got burnt would be used to blacken the girl's faces. You know, Joe, when you think of it, all our harvest celebrations, with the corn dollies in the background, are really celebrations to honour Ceres, the goddess of the harvest! But they are good fun – as one account said, "The ale is good, the lasses are bonny, slim of the waist and light of the foot – and all Yorkshire!"'

HARVEST FESTIVAL

'You know what I like most about the harvest?' said Joe. 'The harvest festival. Has Grandad mentioned it? It's hardly lore, is it? I mean, almost every village still has one.'

'It's here,' Jack beamed. 'He does make the point that a harvest festival in church is a fairly new idea, started in 1843. The vicar of Morwestow in Cornwall, Reverend R. S. Hawker, invited parishioners to a service he had just devised. He called it Harvest Thanks-Giving and allowed his congregation to receive Holy Communion in bread made from the brand-new corn. Other parishes soon followed his example and now it is emulated by all denominations and is very much a part of any parish calendar. Often, as we've said, mell suppers follow in the parish hall, and the churches and chapels are decorated with samples of the harvest such as wheat, barley, oats and fruit and vegetables of all kinds. And a corn dolly! It's a lovely community event, and in most cases the produce is afterwards given to charities.'

GARDENING AND HUSBANDRY

'You know,' said Joe as he drained his glass. 'Grandad's done us all a favour by keeping these notes. What else has he included?'

'There's some more jottings about gardening and husbandry, with some old gardening tips,' Jack said. 'Have a look through the book and see if you can add anything later.'

'Right,' smiled Joe. 'Now let's see these jottings.'

Jottings from the farm

June 11th – St Barnabas' Day. Start haytime because 'on St Barnabas, put the scythe to the grass'.

June 24th – St Johns's Day. Midsummer Day. Cut your thistles before St John/And you'll have two instead of one. Also:

> Cut thistles in May
> They'll grow in a day;
> Cut thistles in June
> They'll come again soon;
> Cut thistles in July
> They will surely die.

If the cuckoo sings on St John's Day, the harvest will be late.

July 25th – St James' Day.

Till St James' Day is past and gone
There could be hops, or there could be none.

August 24th – St Bartholomew's Day. Bartholomew fairs held on this day.

> If St Bartholomew's be fine and clear
> You may have a prosperous autumn that year.

SAM'S OLD GARDENING TIPS

Blow pipe smoke on your gooseberries, and it will keep the wasps off. Pig blood and cow muck are good fertilisers and a ring of fireside ash stops caterpillars climbing up the tree.

Light bonfires under your apple and plum trees, or under other trees. The smoke will keep away pests. Wood smoke is also good for preventing colds, I've heard.

Make a circle of creosoted string on the ground around each cabbage stalk, and it will keep off cabbage fly.

Mothballs crushed and mixed with the earth will keep off carrot fly.

Collect a thin layer of earth and fallen pine or spruce needles, and place the mixture around your strawberries. It makes them taste better.

Keep a clump of nettles growing in the garden or on the farm, preferably on the compost heap. They provide the earth with lots of nutrients (iron, nitrogen, silica, protein, chlorophyll, phosphates and salts), and when close to other plants, will help the others to grow. They will assist the compost to rot, but will need careful control. People used to believe that nettles saved the home from lightning, and you can make soup, cures and hair-restorer from the leaves; if you pack fruit, especially tomatoes, among nettles, they will keep their bloom and freshness, and will last longer. You can use the stings to cure rheumatism, and in some drastic cases, people were thrashed with nettles for this purpose. In days gone by,

women made cloth from the stems, and a clump of nettles attracts butterflies to the garden. Most useful plant, it is! No wonder it is sometimes called Jack-of-all-Trades.

Moles can be kept at bay by planting caper spurge in the garden. There must not be a barrier, like a wall or path, between the moles and the plant, otherwise it will not work. On the farm, we find the best way of clearing moles is to put a hosepipe into a mole run, and fix it to a car exhaust. Run the engine so that it pumps fumes through the mole tunnels – that will shift them. Or you can put mothballs in the runs, or holly leaves – they prick their snouts!

Soapy water (not detergent), left over from the bath or washing up, is good for keeping cabbages free from insect pests.

Unrinsed milk bottles can be filled with water which is then poured on to the garden or into flower pots. It is better than plain water.

If you want butterflies in the garden, plant a buddleia and they will flock to it. It's called the butterfly bush for that reason. Nettles attract peacock butterflies and tortoiseshells, while stacked timber will shelter those butterflies that hibernate, as well as other hibernating insects such as ladybirds.

St Bartholomew brings the dew.

As St Bartholomew's day, so the whole autumn.

St Bartlemy's mantle can wipe dry
All the tears St Swithin can cry.

September 21st – St Matthew's Day.

St Matthew shuts up the bees.

St Matthew brings cold weather and rain.

September 29th – St Michael the Archangel.

The Devil puts his foot on brambles on St Michael's Day. The Devil spits on brambles on this day. Don't pick brambles on or after today, they are past their best but some are OK until October 10th, the old Michaelmas Day.

October – Always put manure on your fields in October to make sure they yield their best the following year.

October 18th – St Luke's Day. Look out for St Luke's Little Summer for there are generally a few days of very warm and sunny weather around this time. But it won't last!

October 31st – Hallowe'en. Apples, pears and other trees can be planted now. A verse says: 'Plant them at Hallowtide and command them to grow; plant them at Candlemas, and entreat them to grow.'

Christmas Day – If the sun shines through the apple trees on Christmas Day, the next autumn will have a very good crop for display!

Names around the Farm

Grandad's notes on names read:

'Lots of names are changing. We still call our cow-shed the "shippen" or the "mistle" but there's other names most of us have stopped using. The partition between the cows is the "skelbeast" and when we swill out the shippen with cold water, we say it's been "sowled out" or we're giving it a good "sowling". When a cow is milked till she's dry, we say she's been "stripped" and the cowman of old was known as "nowterer".

'"Assriddlings" are the fire ashes which we sift; we keep the bigger ones for further burning; I put some of the smaller ash on the garden because it's good for the soil (except where mint grows), and in winter, we put ashes on the footpaths to stop them becoming slippery or "slape". If a path is muddy, we say it is "sluthery".

'When the first spring grass arrives we say "Doctor Green has come" because it is such a good thing, and the fields that are put down to grass are called "swathes" or "swathlands". "Fog" means the grass that grows and is left over after haytime, while a "hagmist" is the fog that is like a low cloud, and a "hime" is a hoar frost.

'A "cowl" is a rake, a "gripe" is a three-pronged garden fork or a muck fork, and a "hack" is a hoe. The basket I used as a lad for sowing corn was the "hopper", the corn stack is a "pike", things piled up, like piled-up straw are called "desses". The stack yard is known as the "staggarth" and the foldyard is the "foldgarth". The place we keep the animal feed is the "fodder house", and some of these names are still used.

'Our morning break is "'lowance time" and work done badly was known as being "sluppered". The "daytal" man was hired by the day and anybody who worked left-handed was called "cuddy-handed". The boss worker was the "hind" or "gaffer" but the master was always the "maister".

'A "down-gang" is a steep path and a "trod" is a footpath, such as a foot-trod, bridle-trod, packhorse trod or monks' trod.

'"Eldin" or "kindling" is firewood, but dead sticks gathered from the bottom of a hedge are "garsil". A "fireflowt" was a spark that flew out of the fire. We called the fireplace the "firestead", a poker was a "firepoat" and we called the bellows that we used, or those the blacksmith used, a set of "firecods".

"'Thack" means to thatch a corn stack and the man who did this was the "theaker"; one of the objects he used was a "thack-prod". This was a pointed peg to which he fastened the "thackband" which secured the thatch. "Staddles" are stones that the stack stands on. They are short, thick stone pillars about 2ft 6 inches tall with a larger top, shaped rather like giant mushrooms. They are positioned in the shape of the base of the stack, and wooden planks are laid over them. Then smaller branches are laid over this framework, and the stack is built on top. It is done to keep rats and mice from climbing into the stack, and it keeps it off the wet ground. The rats and mice can't climb over that mushroom top.

'My favourite words are "graithing" and "fettling" or "fettle". Graithing means mending something or even finishing off an article you've made. "Graithing a plough" means servicing it, making it right, mending it. Fettle also means to fix something, to mend it, to fettle it. It can mean condition as well, such as "What fettle are you today?" (this means "How are you?"); or you might say "When I bought this car, it was in real good fettle." If a doctor cures somebody, you'd say "He fettled him good and proper" – or fettle can mean to deal with something. Fettling the garden means tidying it or working upon it; fettling dinner means preparing it while "fettling for off" means getting ready to go out.'

'You know,' laughed Joe when Jack had finished this, 'it's a good word is fettle; it means whatever you want! Shall we fettle some more whisky?'

Measuring the Land

Grandad's notes said that because Britain had gone into the Common Market, and hectares had been introduced, he'd better make a note about acres before they were forgotten.

'The standard English acre contains 4 roods, each rood containing 40 poles or perches, and each pole containing 272½ square feet. An acre is therefore 4,840 square yards. When we've dealt in land, that is buying, selling or renting (when you buy land, you must always remember you buy a few stones with it!), we've always used this standard acre. But there are other acres, called customary acres and every county or region has its own variation.

'Up in Beckindale, though, we still call Yorkshire the County of Broad Acres, not the County of Broad Hectares!'

'Fascinating stuff,' said Joe. 'There's more, I hope?'

'Oh, aye,' said Jack. 'Lot's more. Grandad's picked the brains of nearly everybody in the village.'

'Show me some other time,' Joe said. 'I must be off!'

'And see if you can add anything to it!' said Jack.

'I will,' said Joe. 'I will. See you.'

CHAPTER THREE

ON HOME HEARTH AND HEALTH

There is little choice among rotten apples.

Sam Pearson's notebook

J ack was seated in his favourite chair before the fireside at Emmerdale Farm, and he was concentrating on the pages of Grandad's notebook.

'Ma,' he looked up at his mother, who was making bread on the kitchen table. 'Have you seen this book of Grandad's?'

'I've not read it,' she admitted, 'but I knew he was making notes about things that went on around him. He wanted to make sure his grandchildren and his great grandchildren and those that followed them knew about the world that he lived in.'

'There's a lot of stuff concerning the house. He's got a section about the domestic side of living, household matters, cooking, bits and pieces about the table, the kitchen, clothes, some simple cures. That sort of thing.'

'Aye,' her eyes misted over at the memory of her father. 'Dad would keep asking me questions about what I was doing and why I did certain things, like warming the pot before I mashed the tea, or why I said "Keep your fingers crossed" when I took cakes out of the oven. For a time, I wondered why. Then he said he was making a record in that notebook, jotting things down, he said, in case folks forgot them for ever. He never showed it to me, though. Not once.'

'It's his private record, Ma. Or it *was* private. I'm sure he wanted us to find it one day, otherwise why keep it? Why spend years compiling it if he didn't want it read?'

'Mebbe he thought we'd not appreciate it when he was alive, Jack. You know how secretive he could be.'

'I'm right glad he did keep it! So, Ma,' he grinned wickedly. 'Why *do* you cross your fingers when you take the cakes out? We all do it sometimes, don't we? For luck.'

'That's why I do it, Jack, hoping my cakes will turn out all right.'

'But it doesn't make any difference, does it?' he pressed her. 'Your cakes will turn out all right whether or not you cross your fingers! It doesn't make a scrap of difference. It doesn't make sense either.'

She smiled at him and suggested, 'See what Grandad says about it.'

He flicked through the pages that dealt with domestic matters, found the entry and read it aloud to his mother.

'Crossed fingers mean good luck. The second, or index, finger was crossed over the forefinger to prevent bad luck when a solitary magpie flew into sight, or when any other thing was done where some good fortune was needed. Starting the car on a frosty morning, our Annie baking bread or cakes, Dolly making wishes when Matt was coping with new lambs, folks sitting exams or buying raffle tickets! They all keep their fingers crossed so that things will go right. It comes from the days when the sign of the cross was used to keep away the Devil and evil spirits; if the people couldn't find a cross, they used to make one the quickest and easiest way possible, by crossing their fingers.

'Other things were associated with hands – people would (and still do) spit on their hands before doing an important job with them. Centuries ago, that was done to bring good luck – it was done as an offering of your soul to the gods! People would do it before fighting; now boxers do it, for example. And spittle was often used to ease cuts and spots.'

'You know, Ma,' Jack added, 'I've often done that. Spat on my hands before tackling a tough job. 'Anyway, Grandad says you should never shake hands across the table and if two people say the same word at exactly the same time, they should link their little fingers together, right hand to right hand, or left hand to left hand, and make a wish. This must be done in total silence; if you speak before linking your little fingers, the wish will not be granted!'

Annie Sugden

Annie smiled. 'We had to do that if we found the wishbone in the chicken!' she told Jack. 'That's the Y-shaped bone near the neck. We linked our little fingers around the shortest bits of the bone and we had to break it. The one who got the biggest piece could make a wish.'

'I'm going to see what else he's got in here, Ma, but first tell me, why do you warm the teapot? Is there a reason, or is it just a custom? Or superstition?'

'It makes the tea better,' she said simply. 'I told Dad this for his book – to make a good cup of tea, the pot should be dry before you start, and you first heat the teapot.

'You pour hot water into it, leave it for two minutes or so and then throw it out. Then you use one teaspoonful of tea leaves for each person, and one for the pot. That's always been the recommended amount. You use water that is freshly boiled – that's very important. It must be fresh and still boiling when you pour it on to the tea leaves

and there's a saying "Water long boiled makes tea spoiled." Some people pour about half the required water on to the leaves and let it stand to "draw" out the flavour before topping up the pot. You shouldn't use a pot that's too big and it's best to pour the tea within five or ten minutes, otherwise it tastes stewed! And if you're drinking one of those delicately flavoured teas, it's best to use an earthenware pot; metal ones don't give the best results.'

'And what about putting the milk in, Ma!' Jack's eyes twinkled with mischief. 'To get the best results, should you put the milk into the cup before the tea, or the tea before the milk?'

'You won't catch me with that one, Jack Sugden!' she laughed. 'It's a matter of taste – some like it one way, some the other.'

'But the milk should always go in first...' he started.

'Jack! No more! Now, what else does Grandad say? I remember him asking me

THE TABLE

'Spilling the salt at table was always unlucky, and if you knocked over the salt cellar while passing it to somebody else, it meant the pair of you would soon quarrel. For the person who actually spilt the salt, it meant bad luck or some other unpleasant result.

'You could prevent this by throwing a pinch of the spilt salt over your shoulder. Some would counteract this bad luck by making the sign of the cross with their knife and fork. If you look at copies of Leonardo da Vinci's painting of The Last Supper, you'll see that Judas has accidentally overturned a salt cellar which is by his arm and look what happened to him!

'Salt used to be a symbol of friendship and if it was spilt, it signified a break in that friendship. That's true with Judas, so it shows how long this idea has been around. You should never put salt on another's plate, either – there's an old saying "Help me to salt, help me to sorrow."

about our table customs. Has he put them in? I know he kept asking questions about them.'

'The only thing I remember as kids was you telling us to say please and thank you at table, and not to get down until we'd got permission from you or Dad!'

'And more besides that!' she laughed. 'Dad would never have thirteen at table, you know. Whenever we had a big gathering at Christmas or for a birthday, he'd always count us first and wouldn't let thirteen sit down together. He reckoned the youngest would die within a year if we did.'

'But that's daft!' Jack said, turning the pages. 'Anyhow, I should think that out of thirteen people, it's possible that one will die within a year. Besides, how can a number matter that much!'

'I've known him invite somebody from the village – anybody who could come at short notice – just to make the number up to fourteen or more. He said it was because of the Last Supper, when Christ and his Twelve Apostles sat down together; since then, thirteen at table has always been unlucky.'

Meanwhile, Jack had found Grandad's notes about table customs. 'Here we are, Ma. He mentions thirteen, but listen to this.' He read aloud from Grandad's notebook.

'Salt was once very important at table for another reason. It was kept in a huge silver saler (salt pot) in the middle of the table. Guests of distinction would sit above it and those of lower esteem would sit below it. That's how we get the saying "to sit above the salt", meaning to sit in an important place.

'Knives could say things too. If you dropped a knife, it meant a visitor was coming, or, if you were in love, it meant you would break with your loved one. And you should never give a knife away, not even as a present, because it severs a friendship. If somebody wants to give you a knife, or anything sharp like scissors or a razor, give them something in exchange, even just a penny. Then you've bought the knife and the bad luck won't affect you.

'When you're at table, you should never allow knives to cross each other – it's a sign of bad luck and suggests evil intentions against your neighbour. Knives, because they're made of iron, kept witches and bad luck away, so some country folk kept one under the pillow. Mothers would lay a knife near a sleeping child to keep it safe.'

Here Jack paused and smiled. 'That's nowt to do with luck, Ma; knives were weapons, and in the days when you couldn't trust anybody, you always kept a weapon handy. Like under the pillow. And do you know,' he continued, 'why we place our knives and forks on the table in the way we do?'

'No, I don't, except it seems a neat way,' said Ma.

'Well,' said Jack, airing his own knowledge. 'When men were rough and always fighting, they always kept their knife in their right hand, even when eating. Always on guard, you see. But if a man laid his knife down when he was eating, it meant he was friendly.'

'Then we must be a friendly household,' beamed Annie.

Jack now turned to Grandad's item about bread.

'Some country folk always carried a crust of bread in their pockets, to bring good luck. There's an old verse:

If ye fear to be affrighted
When ye are, by chance, benighted;
In your pocket for a trust
Carry nothing but a crust
For that holy piece of bread
Charms the danger and the dread.

'Talking about bread, Ma,' said Jack, looking up from the notebook, 'I see you're baking some now. Why do you cut a cross on the top of each loaf before it goes in the oven?'

'I've always done that, and my mother before me, because it makes it rise better,' she said. 'They say it releases pockets of air that might be trapped in the dough.'

'Not according to Grandad!' he laughed. 'It says here, and I quote, "Many housewives and bakers still mark their bread with the sign of the cross before putting it into the oven. That dates back centuries, when bread (which was so important to every household) was marked with a cross to protect it against evil spirits." He says that some folks thought that if a loaf split at the top while being baked, or had a hole in the middle, it meant there'd soon be a funeral in the family. And it says here that it's unlucky to turn a loaf upside down after cutting it.'

'You should always lay a fresh-baked loaf on its side or even turn it upside down,' Annie retorted. 'That's common sense – it stops the bottom getting affected by the steam that's been trapped underneath.'

'But you do this before cutting it?' smiled Jack.

'Naturally!' she said. 'Otherwise, there'd be no point.'

'You know, Ma, reading this makes me wonder whether we do things because we're following superstitious habits which we've done for centuries, or whether there's a real reason.'

'Happen it's a bit of both, Jack,' she said.

'Like pricking a loaf to see if it's done,' Jack said. He read out, 'You should never use a knife or a fork, but always a skewer. "She who uses a fork or knife will never be a happy wife."'

Annie made no comment, so Jack returned his attention to the notebook and found an item about the baker's dozen, then one about eggs and others relating to more domestic topics.'

THE BAKER'S DOZEN

'The baker's dozen is twelve for the baker and one for the Devil, i.e. thirteen loaves, but there is no superstition attached to this. It comes about because bread was originally sold by weight. Loaves would

shrink after a while and as there were heavy penalties for selling short weight, the baker would always add one extra loaf to every dozen sold. This made up the lost weight. So a baker's dozen is thirteen, and this extra loaf was called the vantage loaf. When breadwomen delivered loaves to the houses, they were given one for every twelve they sold. That was their payment. So that's another reason for the baker's dozen.'

ON EGGS

'When setting eggs under a hen, you should give her thirteen. If not thirteen, then some other odd number. If an even number is set they'll not hatch out, or if they do, they could all be cock-birds. Eggs won't hatch if you've carried them over running water, and the best time for setting hens' eggs is after sunset, but never on a Sunday.

'It's often been said by country folk that there's a proper time for fetching eggs into the house, and for selling them. You're not supposed to bring eggs into the house after dark, and you're not supposed to sell them, or let them out of the house, after dark.

'When you've eaten an egg, the shell must not be burnt; it should always be smashed. If an eggshell is burnt the hen that laid it won't lay any more, but the reason for smashing eggshells dates back years, even to Roman times. Rural folk once thought witches used them for evil spells and for travelling about in, especially to make ships sink at sea. So you smash them – children love to do this by smacking boiled eggs on their tops with a spoon and, when they've finished eating, some knock holes in the bottom as well. That's guaranteed to stop witches – those who smash eggshells aren't troubled by witches, so it must work!

'Even now, some sailors won't mention the word "egg" when at sea – they call them "roundabouts", and they're not supposed to be sold on board ship, or even carried!

'I remember when we always kept the last egg laid by an old hen; it was a good luck charm to protect the other poultry and, for the same reason, we would sometimes keep an egg laid on Good Friday. We reckoned, though, that double-yolked eggs meant a death in the family, and one with no yolk at all was generally unlucky. Some said these were laid by cocks, or that the wind had caused them! I've heard them called wind-eggs by the older folk in the Dales.

'I asked the vicar about the custom of rolling eggs at Easter, and I'll come to this later in my notebook,' Grandad had written.

ON APPLES

'"An apple a day keeps the doctor away" – this must be one of the best-known sayings, and it comes from ages past when people thought they were the food of the gods. For this reason, they thought they must be very good and healthy. The Romans knew they were beneficial and brought them to Britain while the name Avalon, the place to which King Arthur went to get his wounds healed, comes from a Celtic word meaning "island of apple trees". All folklore, here and overseas, links the apple with good health.

'Nowadays, we know apples really are good for us because they're full of calories (for energy) and vitamin C; and when they are eaten with their skins on, they provide fibre and also help to keep down our cholesterol level.

'I've heard it said that an apple eaten before a meal helps to keep your weight down: it fills your stomach and so you want to eat less!

'There's an old belief that you must always rub an apple before eating it. That's because it's been tainted by the Devil – he used the apple to tempt Eve in the garden of Eden. So you should rub it clean before you bite into it – I reckon that still makes sense because of the chemicals and other muck that can settle on apples. It still makes good sense to rub the skins.

'When picking apples here in Yorkshire, we believe one or two should be left on the tree, for good luck.

'We say these are for the birds, but the older generations left them for the fairies and other spirits, so they'd look favourably upon the household. In some areas, they think the apple trees should be touched by rain on St Peter's Day (June 29th) or St Swithin's (July 15th), when it's said the saints are watering the orchards. It means a good crop will follow. But it's a bad omen if there is blossom on the tree at the same time as the fruit, or if there's a second blossom – "A bloom on the tree when the apples are ripe is a sure termination of somebody's life."

'There are folks who still go apple-wassailing in the winter. Some do it on New Year's Day, and others on Twelfth Night. Everybody on the farm goes to the orchard at dusk with things that make a lot of noise, like tins, guns, pans, trumpets and so on. They carry a flask of cider, too. A tree is chosen to represent them all and the party then drinks to its health with some of the cider, the rest being thrown over its roots. They all bow to the tree and then make a terrible noise with the tins and things, shooting the guns into the branches while singing, shouting and dancing around it. The pagans thought this woke up the tree and brought it back to life after winter, while frightening away the evil spirits. The idea was to ensure a good crop. We did it when I was a lad, but not many local folks bother these days. I don't think we did it to make a good crop; we did it because it was a good way of having a bit of fun in winter.

'Another thing with apples was done by love-sick girls; they'd peel the skin in one long piece, believing that if it was thrown to the floor over the left shoulder, it would form the initial letter of their future husband's name. If a girl's broke during peeling, she would never marry.'

ABOUT THE HOUSE

It was clear to Jack that his grandfather had taken immense trouble to collate and write up his notes, but he found a miscellany of notes on household items and recipes grouped under the above heading.

ANNIE'S ELDERFLOWER WINE

One of the best and most refreshing drinks is wine made from the elderflowers. It is very quick and simple. You require 1 gallon of cold water, 1¼ lb of sugar, 7 fresh heads of elderflowers, 2 lemons (sliced), 2 tablespoonfuls of white wine vinegar and a large bowl. The elderflowers should not be washed because this impairs the flavour, but do pick off any insects!

First boil the water and pour it over the sugar, stirring to dissolve it. When this is cold, add the florets of elderflowers, plus the sliced lemons and the vinegar. Cover the mixture with a cloth to keep away insects and leave it for twenty-four hours. Finally, siphon it off and bottle it, but make sure it is firmly corked because it is a very fizzy drink. (Use corks rather than screw-top bottles, which might explode.) It is a truly beautiful drink and can be enjoyed almost immediately; it is excellent on a hot summer's day. If it is left for about four years, it changes into something resembling a lovely hock wine.

Aprons

'Our Annie generally wears an apron when she's working, like all country women do. My mother used to say it was bad luck if it fell off, and good luck if she accidentally put it on back-to-front. These aprons were part of their working dress and they were kept very clean, but if the women had dirty work to do, they wore a rough one on top of their usual one. This was made of hessian, and we called it a coarse apron (in dialect – a cooarse appron).'

Bottery Bushes

'My father and his father before him always liked to have bottery bushes growing near the farm house and outbuildings – the proper name is elderberry. For years, country folk thought those bushes protected buildings from being struck by lightning. Some said the Cross used at the Crucifixion was made of elder wood and that's why it will never be struck by lightning. Another tale is that Judas hanged himself from an elder tree.

'That makes it unwelcome in houses and there's a fungus called Judas's ear which grows on the bark of the elder.

'You should never bring elder wood into the house because it's unlucky – and you should never burn it. "Make a fire of an elder tree and death within a year you'll see." One reason for not burning it, is that the wood smells awful, but they do say that sprigs of elderleaves keep the flies off! An infusion of the leaves also makes a useful insecticide.

'The wood does have its uses, though. It is very tough and was once used for making cog wheels for mills and farm machinery and also for toys, butchers' skewers, pegs, bellows and musical instruments. It is hollow, too, and was once used for making water pipes and drains.

'For centuries, the bark, leaves and berries have been used to make medicines "against all infirmities whatever" and I think the juice of the berries is still used in modern lotions, especially to aid the eyes, the skin and the complexion. The berries contain lots of vitamin C, and hot elderberry juice made from the berries is a good cold cure. They can also be used to make a wine which is rather like port. And in summer Annie used to make an excellent wine from the elderflowers. I've included the recipe in my notes. There's no wonder I've always liked bottery bushes around Emmerdale Farm!'

Brambles

'Our Annie makes the best bramble pies for miles around. Other folks call them blackberries or even bumble kites, but they're brambles or brammels to us. I've said earlier that you're not supposed to pick them or eat them after Michaelmas Day (September 29th), but some think this advice is for the Old Michaelmas Day, October 11th. By then, brambles are overripe and often infested with insects but the old idea was that the Devil spat on them after Michaelmas!

'When the daleswomen used to spin their own wool they'd walk miles through bramble patches, picking up the stray bits of sheep wool caught on the briars. There's still a lot about, but women don't collect it now; birds often do, for lining their nests.

'I've still memories of the old cures involving brambles. If a child was suffering from whooping cough, you had to find a natural arch of the bramble, and make the child crawl through, from east to west, sometimes three times and sometimes nine times. As the child passed through, he or she had to chant "In bramble, out cough; here I leave my whooping cough." That was supposed to be a remedy; also, bramble leaves, placed on swellings or burns, were said to cure them.'

Cleaning in the Spring

'My dear wife would never start spring cleaning until May had finished, and I still don't know why!'

Lavender

'To keep clothes fresh and to keep moths away, Annie puts a lavender bag in each drawer and wardrobe. They say that even lions and tigers calm down at the scent of lavender! You can easily make lavender bags. Pick the lavender while it is still in flower and, with the flowers still on their stems, spread it on a newspaper. Leave it to dry. When it is very dry the flowers will come off the stalks easily, and you can fill little muslin bags with them. They will produce a wonderful scent for a long time.'

New Clothes

'We always got nipped when we put on our new clothes. Visitors to our house, like my own grandparents, would say "Nip for new" which meant good luck. We always bought our new clothes in time to wear them on Easter Sunday – you were always supposed to wear new clothes at Easter. There's a verse that says, "At Easter let your clothes be new/Or else, be sure, that you will rue."

'This was because Easter is a new beginning, and the poor folk could only afford one new item each year. Lots of them used to get up early and dress in their new clothes, then go and watch the rising sun. They said the sun danced on Easter Sunday. One funny custom in North Yorkshire used

MAKING A YORKSHIRE PUDDING

The best puddings depend on the way they are mixed and who is mixing them, but here's one way of making good Yorkshire puddings. They say a good Yorkshirewoman never weighs her ingredients as her instinct tells her how much to use, but this is the recipe for some fine puddings.

You need 4 oz of plain flour (it must be plain flour and not self-raising), one egg, a pinch of salt, and half a pint of liquid which is a mixture of one third water and two thirds milk. This is enough for twelve to fifteen small puddings. The oven should be at 425°F or 220°C (Gas Mark 7).

Mix the flour and salt in a bowl. Make a hollow in the centre and pour in a little of the milk and water. Break in the egg and beat with a fork, gradually working in all the flour. Add more liquid as required until all the flour has been incorporated. The mixture should be like a thick pouring batter. Continue to beat well until large bubbles appear on the surface. Then allow the batter to stand for 30 minutes. Put a small blob of lard or beef dripping into bun tins and heat in the hot oven for a few minutes until the fat smokes. Pour about three tablespoons of the batter into each tin and cook for ten minutes until golden brown.

Then eat them straight from the oven and afterwards say, 'Ee by gum, they're grand!')

to be that if a girl went out alone before the church service on Easter Sunday, any boys she met would remove her shoes! After church, this was not allowed.

'My own grandad always put money in the right-hand pockets of his new clothes long before he actually wore them, to make sure he always had enough cash on him. It's also said to be lucky if you put on an item of clothing inside out, and unlucky if you fasten a button in the wrong hole or put a stocking on the wrong foot.

'We always say "Ne'er cast a clout till May is out" – a clout being the old word for a piece of clothing.

'Talking of clothes, there's a good use for socks if you've a sore throat. Take a sock off and wrap it straight away around your neck, and that's supposed to cure it.

'And we've a good saying in Yorkshire about folks that dress up smartly – we say "It's no good being nowt and looking nowt!"'

The Fireside

'If a cat sits with its back to the fire, it forecasts either rain or snow. If a fire is difficult to light it means bad weather, but once it gets going in bad weather it generates more heat. A fire is also said to burn brighter and throw out more heat just before a storm and also if it's going to be windy. Our blacksmith always worked during a storm when he wanted more heat from his fire.

'And you can tell the forthcoming weather by the appearance of the household fire. If it burns dull it means rain or dampness, but if it burns very brightly in winter it indicates frost and clear weather. This also applies if the coal quickly turns to ash. If the coal is covered in thick white ash in winter, it often means snow is on the way, while in summer, it means rain. Before snow comes, wood in the fire will crackle and pop a lot, and if the fire is alternately bright and dim, it means a storm is approaching.

'If sparks stick to the poker or if soot falls down the chimney, it is generally a sign of rain. And if soot burns at the back of the chimney, that's a sign of a coming storm.

'If the smoke from the chimney falls to the ground, that's a sign of rain; if it clings to the roof and follows the eaves, then expect rain within twenty-four hours. Smoke rising straight into the sky means a fine day tomorrow.'

Pins

'"See a pin and pick it up/All the day you'll have good luck;/See a pin and let it lie/All the day you'll have to cry."'

ON PUDDING AND PORRIDGE

Among the wealth of material, Grandad had also written, 'I've been fortunate in having women around me who knew how to cook but some lesser-known recipes and ways of eating get overlooked. I thought I'd best make notes of some of these things, and Annie helped me compile this part of my notes'.

Yorkshire Pudding

'There is often an argument about when and how to eat Yorkshire pudding. It should be eaten before the main course, on its own, fresh from the oven with hot onion gravy. There is no other way to do it properly.

'Southerners make such awful Yorkshire puddings that they have to eat them with the

main course to disguise their ghastliness! If you have a proper Yorkshire pudding, which is so light that it melts in the mouth, you'd never want to spoil it by eating it with anything else.

'Even so, some people have daft ways of eating them. I've even heard of Yorkshire folk who eat them before the meal with sugar and milk or cream, or with sugar and home-made redcurrant wine. I've even heard of them eating Yorkshire puddings with sugar and cream, followed by Yorkshire puddings with onion gravy, and then the main course.

'People would offer the pudding this way because there's an old Yorkshire saying: "Them that eats t'most pudding can have t'most meat." The pudding was the cheapest part of the meal and the idea was to fill the guests so full with pudding that they'd not want much meat!

'Another way was to eat Yorkshire puddings as sweets after the main course, with milk and sugar, or with any other sweetener like honey or treacle. Nowadays, people fill Yorkshire puddings with all manner of things, savoury and sweet.

'They eat them before a meal, during a meal and after a meal, but I reckon it's to disguise their poor efforts at making real Yorkshire puddings.

'One way of making a Yorkshire pudding lighter in winter is to use snow instead of water when mixing the batter.'

Fat Rascals

'The Fat Rascal was once unknown outside Saltburn-by-the-Sea. Until 1974, this town lay within the North Riding of Yorkshire, but is now part of Cleveland County. They used to be served at the Ship Inn and a guide dated 1848 said "In observance of a laudable and prescriptive usage, make it a point of duty, at least once, to eat Fat Rascals and drink tea at Saltburn."

'A Fat Rascal is a small cake similar to a tea cake, and the principal ingredients are lard and flour, sometimes with currants added. (In some areas, butter is used instead of lard.)

'This is the recipe. The ingredients are: 1¼ lb flour, ½ lb lard, three teaspoonfuls of baking powder, ½ lb currants, 3 oz sugar, yolk of 1 egg, milk, water, a good pinch of salt. Rub the lard into the dry ingredients. Mix with equal parts of milk and water to form a paste. Roll out 1 inch thick. Cut with a small cutter. Brush with the yolk of egg. Bake in a moderate oven for 25 to 30 minutes.' Serve warm or cooled.

Plum porridge – for a big party!

'I've found this 1764 recipe if anyone is brave enough to attempt it. It is a curious mixture of meat and fruit, and may be the forerunner of our plum pudding. It emerges as a kind of fluid Christmas pudding.

'"Take two flanks of beef, ten quarts of water, let it boil over a slow fire till it be tender.

'"When the broth is strong, strain it, wipe the pot and put back the broth. Slice into it two penny loaves, cutting off the tops and bottoms, and cover it; let it stand for quarter of an hour, then put in four pounds of currants. Let them boil a little, then put in two pounds of raisins and two pounds of prunes, and let them boil until they swell. Then put in one quarter of an ounce of mace, a few cloves, beat fine and mix it with a little water and put in your pan also one pound of sugar, a little salt, a quart or better of claret and the juice of two or three lemons or verjuice. Thicken it with sago."

'I wonder if this was the "cake of plum" mentioned in a poem published in York in 1662? You had to share the cake of plum with friends and neighbours, and our Annie still makes everybody take a turn in stirring her Christmas pudding mixture. That makes it lucky.'

Frumetty

'Frumetty, which is called frumenty, furmety or furmenty depending where you live, is a traditional Christmas dish which is still eaten in parts of Yorkshire. The principal ingredient is pearled wheat, which should be left overnight to soak in water so that it is ready for use on Christmas Eve. Once the wheat (which is in its husk) has creaved, i.e. swollen due to the soaking, it can be cooked. This is done in a slow oven, where the wheat is placed in water and milk, at the rate of 1 pt of mixed milk and water to 1 lb of wheat.

'Some 3 hours should be allowed for it to cook slowly and it should be ready at midnight, as a thick gruel, rather like a heavy milk pudding. Flavouring can be added as required and this may be liqueurs, rum, brandy, fruit such as currants or sultanas, spices like nutmeg or cinnamon, or even honey and plain sugar. These are simply stirred in, although fruit should be given time to soften after being added.

'Frumetty can be eaten hot or cold, although the recommended way is to have it hot with cream on top. Not everyone likes frumetty but, by tradition, it is eaten while sitting around a blazing log fire on Christmas morning after returning from Midnight Mass. Other dishes to be eaten at this time are mince pies, or gingerbread and cheese. Or a little of each!'

NOTES AND QUOTES FOR THE HOME

'Keep a whole onion hanging in the kitchen, because it will keep diseases away, but never let a cut onion remain in the house. It brings bad luck. (In fact, it attracts germs!)

'Never carry a spade through the house on your shoulder – it's unlucky. (Our Annie says it drops muck all over!)

'Them that won't repair their gutters will soon have a whole house to mend.

'You never appreciate water till the well dries up.

'Good luck doesn't come; it has to be fetched, and it comes only through a sweaty shirt! (That means good luck is often due only to hard work.)

'Men rule the world, but women rule men, and it's men that make houses, but women that make homes!'

CHAPTER FOUR

ON SAINTS AND SUPERSTITIONS

*The sound of church bells is reckoned
to chase away thunder and lightning.*

Sam Pearson's notebook

C ome in, Sandie.' The vicar of Beck-indale, Reverend Donald Hinton, held the door open. 'I was just brewing a coffee, you'll have one?'

'Thanks, yes,' and Sandie Merrick step-ped into the Vicarage. Hinton showed her into his study, where his desk was littered with paper, and offered her a chair.

'I won't be a tick,' he said.

'Shall I be looking at those items of furniture while you're doing the coffee?' she suggested. She had been summoned to the Vicarage to value some pieces of surplus furniture which the vicar was thinking of selling at Hotten in the near future.

'Yes, now that's a good idea. They're all in that room along the passage, first left.'

It took her about ten minutes, during which time Donald Hinton arrived with her coffee; he waited patiently with the mug in his hands as she worked, and then escorted her back to his study.

'There's some nice pieces in there,' she said. 'I should think the corner cupboard will fetch between £200 and £300, and that sideboard a fraction less. I'll send you an official valuation form, Mr Hinton, with each item specified. But if you want a figure now, I should say the sale will realise just under £1,000, less commission of course.'

He settled at his desk and bade her take a seat as she relaxed with her coffee.

'You look busy, Mr Hinton,' she said, looking at his littered desk. 'I won't interrupt you.'

'Oh, no, I'm not really. I've been looking through some notes I made for Sam Pear-son's collection of folklore. I sent them to him at Emmerdale before he died, and I understand he left the notes to Jack. I was checking I'd sent everything.'

'I hadn't heard about that.' Sandie showed interest in this topic. 'What sort of things does it include?'

'Well, in my case, it was saints' days and church lore, but I do know Sam has included the weather, something about animals and local country lore. That sort of thing. I don't suppose you come across much in the salerooms?'

'Actually, Mr Hinton, we do. Not a lot, I admit, but enough to make life interesting. You've no idea how many cracked mirrors we receive for sale because people still think that if they crack a mirror, they're in for seven years' bad luck. I've known women remove mirrors from nurseries in case their new baby saw itself in the mirror; apparently the mums think that if a baby catches sight of itself before it's a year old, it'll not lead a healthy life!'

'I've come across that in death too, Sandie. People would cover a mirror with a cloth if it was in the room where someone had just died; that goes back to the idea that the next person to see themselves in that mirror will also die.'

'Beds are another thing we've had in for sale. One woman brought a little bed in for sale because she'd moved into a bigger house; she wanted a big bed which would fill her bedroom so that she couldn't get into bed at one side and out at the other. She honestly believed you should never get out of bed on the wrong side; you should always get in and out on the same side!'

'There's still a lot of superstition about turning the bed,' Hinton said. 'I know women who will never turn a bed or a mattress on a Sunday or a Friday, and it's said that three people should never help each other to make the bed. Two is OK, but three means that one will die within the year!'

'Chairs too!' Sandie laughed. 'One woman came in with a dining chair and said she'd had her sister staying; the sister had placed it against the wall of her cottage before leaving. Apparently, that's a sign of bad luck and in this woman's eyes it meant her sister would never come again, so she

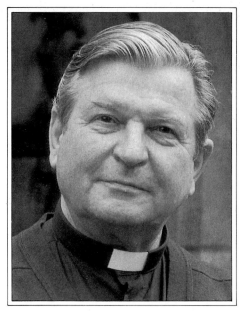

Rev. Donald Hinton.

thought the chair was unlucky; she wanted rid of it.'

'I know that in some hospitals they say that if a nurse knocks a chair over, a new patient will soon arrive, but if a house guest knocks over their chair when leaving a table, they have been telling lies during the meal! And, talking of hospitals, Sandie, there is one at Harrogate where I sometimes go to visit parishioners, and they will not allow a bunch of mixed red and white flowers to be taken into any ward.'

'For superstitious reasons, you mean?'

'Well, they say it upsets the patients. It's a very prevalent prohibition at hospitals even today, Sandie, and it goes back centuries; apparently, a bunch of mixed red and white flowers within a ward means someone there will die. White flowers are said to foretell death, and red symbolise blood. I do know that some florists have been told by hospitals to avoid selling this mixture to visitors!'

'Another thing we get in for sale are clocks, Mr Hinton, especially grandfather clocks when their owners say they've stopped because someone has died. One chap said his had struck thirteen and he wanted rid of it because it meant someone would die.'

'Oh, yes, a lot of people believe clocks stop upon the death of a member of the household, and here in church some older members of my congregation believe that if the church clock strikes during my sermon, or even during the last hymn, there will be a death in the parish within the week.'

'So what other church lore have you found?' she asked.

'Well,' he smiled, 'I could deliver a sermon about bells! In fact, I might just do that! Now, church bells are rung to impart information, to tell the congregation that a service is due to start or, in the case of the last war, to tell us that our country was being invaded. But there are other notions about the ringing of church bells that I've told Sam about for his notebook.'

'Tell me why you ring bells at a funeral.

THE SOUND OF CHURCH BELLS

Bells have always been linked with death and funerals, and our superstitious ancestors thought the noise chased off evil spirits. When a person died in pagan times, lots of noise was made to frighten off those evil spirits and give the dead person a safe passage to the hereafter. Similarly, and no doubt based on this belief, the early Christians felt the sound of bells protected them on this earth, and on their trip to heaven. They felt it kept the Devil at bay, and because they worried that the Devil might destroy the church by lightning, it made sense to protect it by ringing bells during a thunderstorm! This practice gave rise to the saying 'The sound of church bells will chase away thunder and lightning'.

The passing bell, isn't it?'

'No, the passing bell was rung when a person was at the point of death, Sandie. It asked the parish to pray for the soul of the dying person; this is not the bell that is rung after a funeral. That bell is rung as a sign of mourning, and parishes vary the way it is done. Some ring nine times for a man, six for a woman and three for a child. Here in Yorkshire, at Dewsbury, they still ring the Devil's Passing Bell on Christmas Eve. It announces the passing of the Devil as Christ is born and they ring the number of the year – soon it will be 2,000 times.'

'Isn't that a bit pagan, Mr Hinton?'

'The progression from paganism to total Christianity is still going on, Sandie. And we've a long way to go.'

'So what about yew trees in the church-yards. Isn't that a bit pagan? Using them to represent eternal life!'

'I could argue they're not because in the thirteenth century King Edward I ordered yews to be planted in all churchyards to protect the churches against high winds. Now that is a very practical reason. But they do grow very slowly and I admit that many churches are built on the sites of pre-Christian worship. Some of those yews are thousands of years old – they'd be there during the pre-Christian era.'

'But we still use evergreens to symbolise everlasting life, Mr Hinton, even in church at Christmas, such as ivy, holly, laurel and conifers. Surely that is wrong?'

'We use them as symbols, Sandie, not magic trees! There is a difference.'

'I suppose so. So what else did Mr Pearson ask about?'

'He was interested in the way that saints' days were used by country folk as important markers for their calendar of work and play. It's still a fascinating mixture of pagan and Christian beliefs. I'll show you examples,' and he turned to the pile of papers on his desk, retrieving some for guidance.

CALENDARS AND SAINTS' DAYS

January

'January. That is named after the Roman god Janus who had two faces, one looking back over the old year and one looking forward to the new. The Anglo-Saxons called it Wolf-monath, when hungry wolves preyed on villages.'

'I once heard Mr Pearson say "As the days do lengthen, the cold does strengthen",' said Sandie. 'He was talking of January.'

'Yes, indeed. I've another saying here – "If January's calends be summerly gay, 'twill be wintery weather to the calends of May". The calends are the first days of the month, by the way. Now, the first of January is New Year's Day – New Year's Day used to be March 25th, Lady Day, until the new Gregorian calendar was accepted in 1752. However, in church terms January 1st commemorates the Circumcision of Our Lord, as well as the Solemnity of Mary, the Mother of God. A reminder of less Christian times is the custom of First Footing.'

'Oh, we still do that,' Sandie said. 'After midnight on New Year's Eve, the first person into a home on New Year's Day must be an unmarried man whose eyebrows do not meet in the middle; he must carry a piece of coal to symbolise fire and light, a piece of silver to symbolise wealth and a piece of bread to symbolise food. In our part of Yorkshire we insist on a dark-haired man, although some areas prefer fair hair. It's done to ensure good luck to the house during the coming year and if a woman is first to enter, it means bad luck. I know that some farmers would take a sprig of mistletoe to the first cow to calve after New Year's Day to bring good luck to the rest of the herd.'

'Quite,' said Hinton. 'All pagan customs, every one! Old customs are most difficult to halt! Now another important January day is Twelfth Night, or Old Christmas Eve, which is January 5th. It used to be a great time for celebrations with plays and parties; Shakespeare wrote *Twelfth Night* for this kind of festivity. It's a time for taking down our Christmas decorations, and the formal end of Christmas is the following day, January 6th, known as the Epiphany.'

'That's a funny name!' Sandie smiled.

'It's from the Greek, meaning manifestation,' he told her. 'In our case, it refers to the revealing of Christ to the Three Wise Men. Now, the first Monday after the Epiphany is Plough Monday, when a lot of vicars bless the ploughs in church. By ancient tradition, it was the day the ploughmen returned to work and in some churches, the ploughmen's guild placed a candle on the altar. The women returned to their work and their spinning on what became known as St Distaff's Day, January 7th. There is no saint

Sandie Merrick

by that name, of course, the distaff being part of their spinning wheels.'

'Isn't St Hilary something to do with universities?' asked Sandie. 'I remember doing something about that at school.'

'Yes,' Reverend Hinton said. 'He was made a Doctor of the Church by the Pope in 1851, but in fact he was Bishop of Poitiers in the fourth century. The Hilary Terms for the University Year and the Legal Year begin around his feast day, which is celebrated on January 13th in the Anglican church.

'Another saint's day in January is that of St Agnes, which is January 21st; sheep were once blessed and on the Eve of St Agnes, love-sick girls would fast all day so they'd dream the name of their future husband. Now old Sam loved sayings about the weather and I've some here:

'St Vincent's Day, January 22nd:

If on St Vincent's Day the sky be clear
More wine than water will crown the year.

St Ananias' Day, January 25th. This is the feast of the Conversion of St Paul and not his feast day – that comes later, on June 29th. It was St Ananias who restored Paul's sight after he was blinded on the road to Damascus. This is the lore:

If St Ananias be fair and clear
It betokeneth a happy year;
But if it chance to snow or rain
There will be dear, all kinds of grain.
If clouds or mist do dark the sky
Great store of birds and beasts shall die
And if the winds do fly aloft
Then wars shall vex the kingdom oft.'

February

'I know February is called February Fill Dyke because of all the rain,' smiled Sandie. 'And I've heard Mr Pearson say that "rain in February is as good as manure" and that "Much February snow, a fine summer doth show".'

'Yes, farmers do welcome rain or snow in February because it's good for the land. The name comes from the Latin "februo", which means to purify through sacrifice, and it is regarded as the month of purification. In ancient Rome, it was added to the then existing ten months and followed December, then in 452 BC it was placed between January and March. As you know, it is our shortest month with only twenty-eight days, although in a leap year, it has twenty-nine. Every so often, there are five Sundays in February – it only happens during a leap year when February 1st falls on a Sunday, as it did in 1824 and 1976. You might care to work out when it'll happen again!'

'Not me!' cried Sandie. 'That's beyond me! I know that farmers have always regarded Candlemas Day as important. That's February 2nd, isn't it!'

'Yes, the Feast of the Purification of the Blessed Virgin Mary, as it is also known, or Candlemas for short. It was the day the country folk put away their winter candles as the nights were getting lighter, and some new ones were taken to church and blessed for the coming year. Snowdrops bloom around this time too, and they are called Purification Flowers or Fair Maids of February.'

'My granny would never let a snowdrop in the house!' Sandie told him. 'She said it meant a death in the family.'

'I've come across that belief many times during my rounds,' said Donald Hinton. 'But really, they symbolise hope and purity. Now, for the farmers, this is the halfway stage of the winter and they know there's a lot of winter yet to come, and so they say "A good farmer has half his fodder left at Candlemas". That shows his wisdom, you see, knowing that snow and storms can arrive later in the month and well into March. Country people place a lot of faith in the weather on Candlemas Day, you know, by saying:

If Candlemas be fair and bright,
Winter shall have another flight;
If Candlemas be shower and rain,
Winter will not come again.'

'My favourite saint's day in February is St Valentine's Day,' mused Sandie. 'I love getting those mysterious cards on the 14th which stress their undying love for me!'

'That's a fairly modern custom, but did you know there are more than 50 saints called Valentine? Two of them were martyred on this date and no one is sure which one is honoured on this day. Perhaps both? Lovers make this their traditional day, and so do the birds; it's said the birds begin their courtship and find their partners on St Valentine's Day, and a lot of them do start singing about now.'

'All very romantic,' sighed Sandie.

'I sent this piece of lore to Sam for his

book,' said Donald Hinton. 'It's about St Matthias' Day which is February 24th, the time, according to tradition, when the plants start to grow. One verse says "If it freezes on St Matthias' Day, it will freeze for a month together", but another verse suggests that "On St Matthias, sow both leaf and grass" and there's a widespread belief that among our plants, the sap starts to rise on St Matthias' Day.'

'My mum used to cook collops in February,' Sandie reminded herself. 'She'd mention things like Collop Monday, Shrove Tuesday, Ash Wednesday and then Lent.'

'That's right,' Hinton agreed with her. 'A collop is a large piece of meat; before the Reformation in England, the Catholics would fast during Lent, and Collop Monday was their last opportunity to have a good feed by eating the last of the meat. Any left over was salted for preservation. Large pieces were eaten along with other meats and vegetables – it was a really fine feast of all good things. Then no more meat was eaten until Easter Sunday. The day after Collop Monday is Shrove Tuesday, better known as Pancake Tuesday. People would eat up the last of other good things like eggs, milk and sweet items, and they did it in the form of pancakes. That tradition is over a thousand years old, and we still eat them as a seasonal delicacy.'

'They have pancake races in some towns where men and women dash through the streets as they toss pancakes out of frying pans! And at Scarborough, there's the annual Shrove Tuesday skipping on the seafront. Anyone can join in – I've done it sometimes. It's started by the Pancake Bell...' smiled Sandie.

'Yes,' said Hinton. 'Before the Reformation, the people had to go to Confession so that their sins were forgiven before Lent. Shrove Tuesday was the day for this; the priest would shrive his parishioners, i.e. give

them absolution, and when they were shrove, they could enjoy their pancakes. The church bells would call them to church, but after the Reformation, those bells became known as the pancake bells, the signal to start cooking pancakes!'

'And what about Ash Wednesday?'

'That is the first day of Lent,' said the vicar. 'In the Roman Catholic church, ashes from consecrated palms from the previous year's Palm Sunday are used to mark a cross on the foreheads of the faithful. It's a reminder that we came from dust and will return to dust. Now Lent continues for forty days and ends on Easter Sunday, which is a celebration.'

'Marry in Lent and live to repent,' smiled Sandie. 'I think every woman knows of that!'

'Yes, because Lent is a time of sorrowing before the death of Christ, marriage was never recommended in those weeks. From the farmer's viewpoint, a dry Lent means a fertile year, and they say that wherever the wind is on Ash Wednesday, it will remain during Lent.'

Pleased that Sandie was showing an interest in his work, and that she was in no immediate hurry to leave, Hinton refilled their coffee mugs.

March

'I used to be amused by the farmers coming into the mart at Hotten in March,' she said. 'They were always chuntering about the weather, saying things like "I allus say that if March comes in like a lion, it'll go out like a lamb, but if it comes in like a lamb, it'll go out like a lion". One of their favourites was "A windy March foretells a fine May" and some said that "March winds and April showers bring forth flowers".'

'The month of many weathers, that's how I've heard it described,' said Hinton. 'It's always been notorious for its blustery and boisterous winds. It's not without reason that it's named after Mars, the god of war, and the Anglo-Saxons called it Hyldmonath, meaning the windy or stormy month. But there are flowers, too, like the daffodil. They're said to bloom on St David's Day – that's March 1st, which is also Whoopity Scoorie Day in Lanarkshire! Winter is chased away by bells ringing and the children staging mock battles with balls of paper.'

'He's the patron saint of Wales,' said Sandie. 'We had a girl at school who always wore a leek and ate leek pie or drank leek soup on St David's Day.'

'I like to see customs kept alive,' said Hinton. 'Now, March 21st is very important from a church point of view. It is the first day of spring, of course, but it is also St Benedict's Day, when we should recall a piece of history made here in Yorkshire. There were problems about determining the date of Easter and so a synod met at Whitby Abbey in AD 664 to discuss it. That famous Synod of Whitby decided to follow the Pope's method and we still follow that ancient ruling – Easter falls on the first Sunday after the first full moon that occurs on or after St Benedict's Day, which is the spring equinox, i.e. March 21st. This means that it falls on a different date every year, but it cannot be before March 22nd or after April 25th. And for gardeners, peas should be sown by St Benedict's Day.'

'You mentioned Lady Day earlier,' Sandie said. 'Is that a church day too!'

'Yes, it was the feast of the Annunciation of the Blessed Virgin Mary, when she was told she was to be the Mother of God. Here in England, it was called Lady Day and was the first day of the legal year until the English calendar changes of 1752. Rents were due, tenancies were reviewed, commenced or terminated and it was New Year's Day. Now, things have changed but some still think that if either Good Friday or Easter Sunday fall on Lady Day, there will be a national disaster within a year.'

Hinton passed Sandie a piece of paper bearing the relevant verse:

If Our Lord falls in Our Lady's lap
England will meet with a great mishap.

April

Sandie noticed that the next sheet of paper in his hands was headed 'April' and she said, 'We had great fun as kids on All Fools' Day, April 1st. We'd play jokes on each other, or on our parents and even the teachers at school until 12 noon. Then we had to stop.'

'April's a lovely month,' beamed Donald Hinton. 'I love it. The name means "to open", signifying the new life among our wild creatures and the opening of buds and flowers. It used to be called Easturmonath after Eostre, a heathen festival in honour of the rising sun. It's said that if it thunders on April 1st, we will have good crops of corn and hay, and then our most famous bird arrives on our shores – the cuckoo. It's said it arrives on Cuckoo Day, which is April 14th, and we follow that with St George's Day.'

'That's April 23rd,' said Sandie. 'Our patron saint, and the patron saint of Portugal and Aragon. Wasn't he demoted?'

'Well, in 1960, the Pope reduced his stature as a saint and abolished his feast day. It seems that his existence cannot be proved even if he did fight dragons! The feast day was replaced by a mention of St George's name in the Mass of the Day but he's still our national patron saint.'

'Farmers call St George's Day a borrowing day,' Sandie told him. 'Around this time, they are able to assess the potential of their crops and so bargain with bank managers for loans based on that value!'

'And there are two peculiar days in April,' said Hinton. 'St Mark's Eve, which is the 24th, and Walpurgis Night, which is on the 30th. On St Mark's Eve and, indeed, on St Mark's Day, superstitious people would sit in the church porch and riddle chaff; they started at midnight on the 24th and it was said they would see the figures of those who would die during the coming year.'

'Easter usually falls in April, doesn't it?' Sandie asked. 'That's a major event for you!'

'With Christmas, it's the most important period of the church year,' Hinton agreed. 'It is preceded by Holy Week or Passion Week, and we have Maundy Thursday, that's the Thursday of that week. We Anglicans sometimes call it Holy Thursday. The name Maundy comes from the wording of the antiphon of the day in the Roman Catholic Latin Mass (*Mandatum novum do vobis* – A new commandment I give unto you). During the Mass, there was a ceremonial washing of the congregation's feet by the priest.'

Hinton continued, 'This commemorates Christ washing the feet of his disciples and until 1689, the Sovereign washed the feet of the poor in Westminster Abbey. Since the time of James II, however, it has been the custom to give money to the poor and this is specially minted money called Maundy Money; it is given to a number of pensioners corresponding in number to the Sovereign's age. In 1953, because Westminster Abbey was being prepared for the Coronation of Queen Elizabeth II, St Paul's Cathedral was used instead and since that time the ceremony has travelled the country, being held

in different cathedrals.'

'I liked Good Friday,' said Sandie. 'We always had hot cross buns and we sang "One a penny, two a penny, hot cross buns". Mum told us that if they were actually made on Good Friday, the cross on them was supposed to protect the house from fire during the coming year. She kept a couple in the kitchen, hanging there until they were dry, and some said these were useful as cures. Pieces were grated and mixed with milk and water, then swallowed. I know some old folks who think that hot cross buns made on Good Friday will never go bad. And my granny would never wash or dry clothes on Good Friday.'

'Sam has included something about gardening on Good Friday, but did your generation roll Easter eggs at Easter?'

'Oh, yes, we loved that. Mum hard-boiled them and dyed the shells with recipes handed down in the family. Me and Jackie rolled them till the shells broke, then ate them.'

'In some areas,' Hinton explained, 'they are called pace eggs or paste eggs. On Easter Saturday, boys would tour the villages performing Pace Egg plays, or entertain with morris dancing in return for gifts of sweets or money. Then Easter Sunday was a time of celebrating the end of the Lenten fast when meat and sweets could be eaten again, and on Easter Monday it was time to roll Easter Eggs. I believe this could have a link with the rolling back of the stone from Christ's tomb, or the cracking of shells could be linked to the heathen idea of eggs opening to begin new life. Anyway, the name paste egg or pace egg comes from Pasch, a derivation of the Hebrew *pesach*, meaning Passover. Pasch eggs were a symbol of the Resurrection.'

Sandie thanked him for the coffee and the time he had spent with her, and said, 'Well, Mr Hinton, I must be going; I've a meeting at

Hotten next. I'll send a detailed evaluation of those pieces of furniture so you can decide whether you wish to dispose of them.'

'Thank you, Sandie, that's most kind.'

When she had gone, he settled down to examine the rest of his notes with a view to making use of some ideas for future sermons. The next few topics were in note form, and the first dealt with May.

May

'Possibly named after Maia, the mother of Mercury, to whom Roman sacrifices were made on the first day of this month. Another likely source of its name are the Roman *majores,* senators to whom the month was dedicated, or it could even come from the Sanskrit *mah*, meaning "to grow". The Anglo-Saxon name was Trimilce, because the cows could be milked three times a day.

'Weather Lore:

1. A swarm of bees in May is worth a load of hay.

2. Rain in May makes bread the whole year.

3. A hot May makes for a full churchyard.

'May 1st – May Day. The Feast of Saints Philip and James the Lesser, and one of the great rural festivals. It has been, and still is, marked in a variety of ways. Maypole dancing still continues in some Yorkshire villages and a popular belief was that washing in dew at sunrise was a guarantee of beauty and of a fine complexion.

'May 3rd. Rowan Tree Day. Sprigs of mountain ash (also known as rowan) were taken indoors to protect the building and its occupants against the Devil, witches and disease. Some were placed in the thatch as a form of fire protection. People carried them to ease rheumatism and grew rowans near the house to protect it against all evil. A rowan twig in the butter churn made it safe, and twigs were hung around animals' necks or horns to protect them from the evil eye. Horsemen made whips out of rowan to safeguard their horses – "woe to the lad without a rowantree gad".

Many rains, many rowans;
Many rowans, many grains.

'May 11th, 12th, 13th, 14th – collectively known as the Ice Saints' Days. They are the feast days of Saints Mamertius (11th), St Pancras (12th), St Gervatius (13th) and St Boniface (14th). It is said there is always frost on the Ice Saints' Days. Two sayings: 1. "Plant your beans on St Gervatius' Day"; 2. "He who shears his sheep before St Gervatius, loves the wool more than the sheep".

'May 25th – St Urban's Day. St Urban brings summer.

'Rogation Sunday. This often falls in May; it is the fifth Sunday after Easter and is followed by the Rogation Days, i.e. Monday, Tuesday and Wednesday. These were once called Gang Days because people would go (gang) around the countryside, beating the parish boundaries. Men took village lads and bumped their bodies against walls or trees, or ducked them in streams and ponds, to impress upon them the position of their own parish boundaries. In this way, the lads never forgot!

'Ascension Day or Holy Thursday in the Catholic Church is when Christ ascended bodily into heaven. Ascension Day often occurs in May, but is always on a Thursday, and one rural custom is well-dressing. Wells are adorned with flowers – this follows an ancient belief that the water-gods required a sacrifice to keep them content, and the church later named wells after saints and called them holy wells. Many believe that water from a well is pure and health-giving.'

June

'The goddess Juno might have given her name to this month, or it may be named after Junius Brutus. The Anglo-Saxon name was Seremonath, the dry month, or the month of haysel.

'Weather Lore:

1. A dripping June sets all in tune.
2. Calm weather in June sets all in tune.
3. If the north wind blows in June, there will be a good corn harvest.

'June 11th – St Barnabas' Day. Barnaby Day. Barnabas was a farm labourer and his day is celebrated by Barnaby Fairs. Before the calendar was changed, June 11th was the longest day, traditionally set aside for haytime. It was known as Barnaby Bright.

Barnaby bright, Barnaby bright,
Longest day and shortest night.

'June 15th. St Vitus Day. (He was also called St Guy.)

If St Vitus Day be rainy weather
It will rain for thirty days together.

(St Vitus is the patron saint of epileptics and those afflicted with chorea, the disease also known as St Vitus's Dance.)

'June 22nd – St Alban's Day. Alban was Britain's first Christian martyr; he was beheaded in AD 287 at Verulamium, now called St Albans. His relics were scattered during the Reformation. "Weeds cut on or near St Alban's Day, in the afternoon or at full moon, will never reappear."

'June 23rd – St John's Day. Midsummer Eve. Druids maintain a midnight vigil before the midsummer sunrise at Stonehenge. This is Mugwort Digging Night, when people dug beneath this plant to seek a magic coal which would protect them against fire and plague. "If it rains on St John's Eve, the nuts will be spoiled". "Before St John's Day, we pray for rain; afterwards, we get it anyway!"

'June 24th – Feast of St John the Baptist. Midsummer Day. Bonfires were lit to encourage fertility in crops and livestock and cattle were driven through the flames to ward off diseases. Bracken seeds were gathered between 11 pm and midnight and placed on a white sheet or upon a bible. It was thought they gave men magical powers.'

July

It was around mid-morning the following day that Jack Sugden called to see Donald Hinton. Hinton invited him in for a coffee.

'I was passing, vicar, and thought I'd drop in. As you know, Grandad was compiling a book before he died, with the help of a lot of friends, and I see you sent him some material. My reason for popping in is to ask if you've any more. I have your notes up to the end of June.'

'How odd, Jack. Yes, young Sandie called yesterday as I was going through my papers and this morning I was reading them as you arrived. I've got to June, so my other notes must be still here. Look, come through to the study and we'll see what I've got.'

Jack settled down as Donald made the coffee. The vicar returned with two mugs, picked up an untidy file and said, 'Yes, here

we are. Two copies of my notes on July right through to the year end.'

'Can I see them?' asked Jack. 'It'll save time if I check now whether anything's been duplicated.'

The first file was about July, the month named by Mark Antony in honour of Julius Caesar. Once known as Quinctillis, it was the fifth month before January and February were added, and the Anglo-Saxons called it Maedmonath, the month when meadows flowered and the cattle were turned into them to feed.

The weather lore was:

1. The English winter ends in July and begins again in August.

2. If the first day of July be rainy, it will rain for four weeks together.

3. Never trust a July sky.

'I've listed the days of interest,' said Hinton. 'They are:

'July 2nd – St Mary's Day. If it rains on St Mary's Day, it will rain for four weeks.

'July 3rd until 11th August – these are the Dog Days, known for being very hot. The Romans thought that Sirius, the Dog Star, rose and set with the sun and gave extra heat during these days.

'July 4th – St Bullion's Day. If the deer rise dry and lie down dry on Bullion's Day, there will be a good harvest.

'July 6th – St Sexburga's Day. Old Midsummer Day. Plant cucumber seeds and you'll have cucumbers, wet or dry.

'July 15th – St Swithin's Day. Swithin was Bishop of Winchester from 852 until 862 and wanted to be buried outside the church.

'He wanted to feel the rain on his body but when the cathedral was finished in 971, his remains were taken inside. It is said the saint wept in protest and legend says if it rains on St Swithin's Day, it will rain for forty days. It's a good sign if it rains on apples on St Swithin's – it's said he blesses them with his tears and there'll be a good crop.

'July 20th – St Margaret's Day. Plant turnips on this day.

'July 22nd – St Mary Magdalen's Day. If it rains on her day, she is washing her handkerchief in readiness for the festival of St James the Great, who was her cousin. It is on July 25th.'

August and September

'That's fine, Donald,' said Jack. 'Now, there's not a lot for August, is there? Like September, it's a quiet month.'

'I've mentioned that the Emperor Augus-

tus regarded August as his lucky month,' said Hinton. 'He called it after himself – he didn't want to be outdone by Julius Caesar's July! It used to be called Sextilis, the sixth month, until January and February were added. I like the Anglo-Saxons' name for August – the Weodmonath, because of the growth at this time.'

'Fine,' said Jack. 'Now a bit of weather lore:

1. Dry August and warm does harvest no harm.
2. So many August fogs, so many winter mists.
3. August ripens, September gathers in.'

Hinton smiled. 'I've included a new piece of lore,' he said. 'Yorkshire Day. That's on August 1st. It commemorates the loss of the three Yorkshire Ridings in 1974.'

'Good for you!' Jack beamed. 'August 1st used to be called The Gule of August and was one of the great pagan festivals when the first fruits of the harvest were celebrated. And, as you well know, Donald, it was Lammas Day, lammas being from Loaf Mass when a Mass was held, with communion wafers made from bread baked with the season's new grain. There's a saying "After Lammas, the corn ripens as much by night as by day".'

'And I've got a couple more,' Hinton added. 'They are:

'August 10th – St Lawrence's Day. "If on St Lawrence's Day the weather be fine, a fair autumn and good wine can be expected". This used to be St Philomena's Day too, until 1961 when the Pope discontinued it due to lack of proof of her existence. Also August 12th – The Glorious Twelfth, grouse shooting starts.'

'Good, and what about September, vicar?'

'Not a lot, Jack. As the name suggests, it was the seventh month in the Roman calendar, and the Anglo-Saxons called it

Gerstmonath, the barley month, or Haefest-monath, the harvest month. There's also some weather lore, for example:

1. September blows soft till the fruit's in the loft.
2. Thunder in September means a good crop of grain and fruit next year.
3. Fair on September 1st, fair during the whole month.

'My notes include:

'September 14th – Holy Cross Day or Holyrood Day, when it was the custom to go nutting. "The devil goes anutting on Holyrood Day".'

Jack noticed the entry for the Feast of St Michael the Archangel and said, 'September 29th, Michaelmas Day. Grandad's got something about that, but I see you mention that rents were due and goose was eaten! That was because Elizabeth I was eating goose when she heard about the defeat of the Spanish Armada and it's always been celebrated by a feast of goose. Actually, the public thanksgiving for this victory was on 20th August 1588. In Yorkshire, Donald, rose hips were gathered that day to make into a drink.'

October

'Now, October, Jack,' said Hinton. 'The lore builds up again for the autumn. October was, of course, the eighth month in the time of Romulus and the Anglo-Saxons called it Wynmonath, which means the month when wine flows. However, it was also called Wynterfylleth, the time winter begins.'

'I see you've got the usual weather lore, Donald:

1. There's always twenty-one fine days in October.
2. Much rain in October, much wind in December.
3. If foxes bark often in October, it means snow.
4. If the oak wears its leaves in October, it heralds a hard winter.
5. Warm October, cold February.
6. In October, dung your fields.'

'One specific statement, Jack, occurs over October 28th which is the feast day of Saints Simon and Jude. It says "There is sure to be rain on this day". I must say I have never checked the truth of this!'

'Hallowe'en, we must include that,' Jack said. 'You'll have summat about it?'

'October 31st – the Eve of All Hallows', Jack, or Samain. The night the spirits of the dead roam the countryside to visit their former homes. Now that belief prevailed among both pagans and Christians, and because it was dark at night, they all lit bonfires in the hope they would give the dying sun a little more strength. Those fires have been transferred to November 5th in the guise of Guy Fawkes' Night. It's a night when ghosts and witches are abroad and Hallowe'en games are played to keep people cheerful. Modern youngsters play "trick or treat" by knocking on doors to ask that question – if you don't give them a treat, like a sweet or coin, they play a trick on you. It's also Nutcrack Night. Lovers would place two nuts on the fireside; if both burnt away, all would be well between them, but if the nuts flew apart or failed to burn, the man was faithless!'

November

'Right,' said Jack. 'This takes us into November, and straight into All Saints' Day and All Souls' Day. All Saints' Day is November 1st, which is a day to honour those saints for whom there is no special day, and All Souls' is November 2nd, when prayers were said for the dead.'

'Absolutely,' said Hinton. 'A follow-on, if you like, from Hallowe'en; soulers would sing a hymn at each house on All Souls' and be given soul cakes to eat. These were spiced buns.'

'Aye, and I remember Parkin Sunday,' said Jack. 'In some parts of Yorkshire, we ate parkin, a kind of pepper cake made from treacle and ginger; that was on the Sunday within the octave of All Saints'.'

Hinton smiled. 'There is a saying that "If on November 1st, the weather holds clear, an end of wheat sowing do make for the year". There is more lore about November:

1. A cold November, a warm Christmas.
2. If there be ice in November to bear a duck
There'll be nothing after but sludge and muck.
3. Flowers in bloom in late autumn indicate a bad winter.'

'A miserable month; it should be the ninth according to its name,' Jack said, reading from the vicar's notes. 'It was ninth in ancient Roman times, and the Anglo-Saxons called it Blodmonath, the month of sacrifice because they slaughtered cattle and preserved the meat for winter. And I see there's even lore on Guy Fawkes' Night, November 5th. Tharf cakes were eaten; these were made from oatmeal, butter and treacle, and could be a relic of a feast in honour of the Scandinavian god, Thor. Following that, I see you've a note about Martinmas, otherwise the feast of St Martin of Tours, which is on November 11th. Grandad's got summat on that.'

'There is a bit of lore,' said Hinton. '"Where the wind is on Martinmas Eve, it will remain for the winter".'

'Farmers have their own lore,' said Jack. 'We say "Wind northwest at Martinmas, severe winter to come" and we allus reckon that "On Saint Martin's Day, winter's on the way".'

'One modern event in November, Jack, is Armistice Day and that falls on St Martin's Day too. It's the eleventh day of the eleventh month and we have a two-minute silence at 11 am, the eleventh hour, to honour the dead of World War I. It is now incorporated in Remembrance Day, which honours the dead of World War II. We usually hold joint memorial services on the second Sunday of November and sometimes call this Poppy Day because red poppies are worn to commemorate the dead of both world wars.'

'Now,' said Jack. 'I see you have one more date: 25th. St Catherine's Day. Cattern cakes were eaten:

Rise, maids, rise; bake your cattern cakes
Bake enough to bake no waste
And let the bellman have a taste.

'St Catherine was martyred on a spiked wheel, and we remember her now with fireworks called Catherine wheels. And,' continued Jack, 'they say "Whatever the weather on St Catherine's Day, so it will be next February". And finally, as they say, St Andrew's Day, November 30th. He's the patron saint of Scotland but this was once Squirrel Hunting Day!'

December

'And that brings us to December, Jack,' said Hinton. 'To that great Christian festival of Christmas.'

'Or the great pagan festival of Yuletide,' laughed Jack. 'It's a difficult job separating one from the other, what with mistletoe, Yule Logs and the like. Anyway, what have you got for December?'

Hinton ignored Jack's taunting. 'It was the tenth month of the ancient Romans,' he said. 'The name reminds us of that, and the Anglo-Saxons referred to it as the Haligmonath, the holy month, or the Wintermonath. I've included a little lore, as follows:

1. Thunder in December presages fine weather.
2. If it rains before Mass on the first Sunday in December, it will rain for a week.
3. December cold with snow is good for rye.'

Hinton continued, 'Obviously, December 6th is important because it's St Nicholas' Day; the name Santa Claus comes from that and because he was a priest, he is also known as Father Christmas. When he was Bishop of Myra in the fourth century, he saved some children from death and secretly gave them presents. Now, of course, he is the patron saint of children.'

'The so-called Halcyon Days come about now,' Jack added. 'The first is December 11th and there are fourteen of them. Halcyon comes from the Greek for kingfisher, and it was thought to lay its eggs on the surface of the sea and incubate them for 14 days. During that time, the sea became unusually calm and so these were called Halcyon Days. We use the term for a period of calm happiness.

'So what else have we?' Jack continued.

'December 21st – St Thomas' Day,' said the vicar. 'The shortest day of the year. Thomas was the famous Doubting Thomas, the apostle who refused to believe Christ had risen until he could touch the wounds made during the crucifixion. They say ghosts are given their freedom on the Eve of St Thomas, but boys on the North York Moors would go A-Thomassing. They'd visit outlying houses asking for pepper cake or ginger bread and cheese. The weather lore for the day is: "Whichever way the wind is blowing, it will remain there for the next quarter".'

'And so to Christmas,' said Jack. 'We decorate our homes with pagan Yuletide greenery like holly, ivy and spruce, and we hang up the Druids' very own magic plant, the All-Heal, or mistletoe, to keep us all friendly.'

'And we also celebrate the birth of Christ by holding church services, giving presents and having family gatherings. It is now Christ's Mass, Jack, a very Christian festival.'

'I can't understand how Christians can make use of pagan symbols, vicar. Anyroad, we all enjoy Christmas for whatever reason.'

Hinton resumed with, 'Boxing Day, otherwise St Stephen's Day (December 26th), was a time for exchanging presents in boxes, and wrens were hunted by boys; some farmers bled their livestock today, believing it was good for their health, and it's said that "A windy St Stephen's Day is bad for next year's harvest". Now, I know you farmers looked forward to St John's Day, that's December

27th, because it was the day for borrowing money. The bank manager could see the result of the harvest and judge whether or not to lend more money to buy seeds for next year. This St John, by the way, was one of the Baptist's disciples before he followed Christ. The day following was also important – it's Holy Innocents' Day, or Childermas, when we remember Herod's slaughter of the infants as he tried to kill the baby Jesus. It's said to be the unluckiest day of the year and that anything started on it will fail. There is a saying "If it be dark, cloudy and wet on Childermas, there will be scarcity. If it be fair, there will be plenty".'

'Then it's December 31st, the end of the year,' said Jack. 'Never let your fire out on New Year's Eve, and never allow your larder to be empty or your pockets without money as the old year goes out. Whatever is empty as the New Year comes in, will remain empty; whatever is full, will continue so.'

'You keep those top copies, Jack,' said Donald Hinton. 'I trust you'll find them useful for Sam's book. I know he did a lot of work on it before he died.'

'He did, but so have folks like you, vicar, and I'm very grateful for your help. He's been to see others, as you know, Seth Armstrong for one! I'm dying to see what Grandad has made of Seth's contributions!'

CHAPTER FIVE

ON WEATHER, WISDOM AND WILDLIFE

The sun sees no difference between rich and poor.

Sam Pearson's notebook

S eth Armstrong was airing his knowledge in the Woolpack when Joe walked in. As Joe went to order a pint from Amos, he could hear Seth speaking to a newcomer at the bar.

'You can learn a lot from foxes. I allus say you'll never catch a fox twice in t'same snare; in fact, I'll tell you what, if it's an old fox, a snare's no good at all. Old foxes never get caught in snares, they're far too crafty for that. If you want to outwit a fox, you've got to be very cunning yourself and there's an old saying that many a fox is hunted, but not many gets caught. In fact, some never see a foxhunt. And there's summat that every young fox soon learns – and it should be a lesson for people an' all – and it's this; if you run after two hares, you'll catch neither. That's good advice for anybody. Make your mind up which way to go, then don't get diverted.'

The man was obviously interested and asked, 'Tell me, Mr Armstrong, is it true that a fox gets rid of its fleas by picking up a mouthful of moss or sheep's wool, then sinking in a river up to his muzzle? I've heard it said that the fleas all try to escape the rising water by clambering on to the moss or wool, and then as the fox sinks underneath, he releases it and it floats off with all the fleas on board. Do they really do that?'

'You hear all sorts of tales about foxes.' Seth sipped his pint. 'Very clever animals, they are,' he said. 'I'll tell you what I've seen 'em do. I've seen 'em run along wall tops during a hunt, keeping their scent off the ground to baffle t'foxhounds. They'll run up beds of rivers and streams an' all, knowing their scent'll not linger on the water, and I've seen one roll himself in farmyard muck to smother his scent. Reynard knows he's got a strong scent – it comes from a gland under his tail – and he knows how to hide it. I've seen one run along the top of a thick hedge, tripping along like a ballet dancer, he was.

And another ran through a cottage, in the front door and out the back into the garden, to give the hounds the slip. Very crafty and fast-thinking they are. Do you know, they can tell if it's going to rain? If they bark a lot and cry out, it means stormy winds are coming, and rain within three days.

'And they'll hypnotise birds. I've seen a fox wait until pheasants start roosting, just when it's getting dark, then he'll creep under the tree and start running round in rings, frisking about and chasing his tail round the tree. The daft birds start to watch him and when he's got their attention, he'll sit still and fix his eyes on just one pheasant; it watches him and he watches it, his eyes never leaving its eyes. If it moves its gaze, he moves to match, and then the bird'll sort of go into a daze and tumble off the branch. It'll be snapped up by the fox, just like that. They'll hypnotise hens an' all in a similar way. Very daft birds are hens and pheasants, very little brains they've got, no match for a clever fox.'

'Stoats will hypnotise rabbits, too, won't they?' the man asked.

'Weasels, more like,' countered Seth. 'When a stoat chases rabbits or hares, they become so terrified they'll just give up running. But if a weasel can't catch his dinner, he'll copy the fox's trick – he'll charm a hedgerow full of small birds, sparrows, finches, bluetits and things, by twisting and turning as if he's doing a snake-dance. It frightens 'em, but they'll come closer and closer, watching his daft antics until they are unable to move and then he'll grab one. And they say you'll never find a weasel asleep. It's said that if weasels and stoats run about a lot during the morning, there'll be rain by afternoon. And it's unlucky if a weasel crosses your path on the start of a journey, but if it runs to the left, it means even worse luck!'

'Really?' asked the visitor, not sure whether to believe Seth's stories.

Seth Armstrong

Now a stoat is the bigger of the two; he's over a foot long, counting his tail, but the female's smaller. They're light brown on top and white beneath, but they've got a black tip to their tails. That easily identifies 'em. They turn white in winter, especially in Scotland and up north, but their tail-ends stay black.

'Ermine, we call 'em then, folks use their furs for trimming lords' and judges' robes. You can tell ermine on robes by the black marks – they're the stoats' tail-ends. White weasels, by the way, are reckoned to be unlucky, and a sign of some coming disaster. Weasels are only nine or ten inches long. They're both cousins of my ferrets, and their other cousins are minks, polecats, pine martens and even otters.'

'Fascinating stuff!' The man was preparing to leave, not knowing whether all this was true, and said, 'You never did tell me about the fox and the fleas, Mr Armstrong.'

'Put it this way,' said Seth. 'I've never seen that happen, so I can't rightly say it does happen, can I? It's one of them country tales that keeps on being told. Some swear it happens. But the other tales are true enough.'

'Thanks for entertaining me,' and the man left with a smile of thanks for Amos. Joe then moved towards Seth.

'Got a minute, Seth?' he asked.

'I've enough time to sink a pint if somebody'll buy me one,' Seth said.

'Two pints please, Amos,' laughed Joe, who then escorted Seth towards a corner table. 'Now, Seth, who's your pal? That was fascinating stuff you were telling him.'

'He's a salesman, just passing through,' said Seth. 'Never clapped eyes on him before, but now I reckon he's just a bit wiser in the ways of animals. Was there summat you wanted, Joe?'

'Aye,' and Joe explained about Grandad's notebook, then asked, 'Did he come to you for help?'

'He was never away, Joe, him and his notebook! Aye, me and him did have some chats about things, the weather, rainbows, wild animals and so on. He took it all down, but he never said why he wanted to know.'

'I just wanted to say thanks. I'm glad folks like you helped him, it's made it possible for Grandad to record a slice of country life, Seth. It'd be lost otherwise. I think that's why he kept asking all those questions.'

'Sometimes I think I've a book in me, Joe, all this knowledge I've gathered up. It's amazing how much you pick up in a lifetime. It's all in my head, so when I go, it'll go.'

'Like what, Seth?' asked Joe.

'Things I never got round to telling your Grandad, Joe, like how to drive moles away or why we should make friends with hedgehogs.'

'So tell me, and I'll see it's added to Grandad's notes!'

MOLES AND HEDGEHOGS

'Right, moles,' Seth began. 'Mouldiwarps or whatever you like to call 'em. Shakespeare made Hotspur call 'em moldwarps but in t'Dales we say mowdies. As you know, Joe, them little heaps o' soil are dangerous to farm machinery, horses can break legs if they step in a hole and they're a right mess on lawns and tennis courts. You can try trapping mowdies – that's the surest way – but you've got to know your job, know how they make their underground runs and so on.

'A good terrier or even a cat might catch a mowdy that ventures on to the surface, but it's best to deter 'em. Now there's all manner o' ways of doing that.'

Seth paused for a long draught of beer before continuing. 'Some stick mothballs down the runs, others pour liquid disinfectants down. One old country way was to put holly, hawthorn or rose stems down the holes so it would prick their noses if they tried to dig past it. Some say they don't like noise or vibration, so that's why they never invade football pitches and cricket fields,

but I reckon that's not true. I've seen cricket pitches riddled with mowdy heaps. You can get poisons and pellets from garden centres these days, and most seem to work well enough.'

'We use poison,' said Joe, 'but we do it through the Ministry of Agriculture, Fisheries and Food. All very formal. I hate having to kill 'em, but sometimes there's no alternative.'

'Aye, well, folks with 'em in their gardens can't be bothered with that sort of carry on,' said Seth. 'So one way is to stick a milk bottle down their holes, open end up. When the wind hums across the neck, it vibrates down the runs and scatters the mowdies, so they say. Years ago, some liked to kill the little blighters because they thought a mowdy's feet, carried about in their pockets, kept cramp and rheumatism at bay. Mowdy blood was said to cure warts, an' all; they'd catch a mowdy, prick his nose to make it bleed, and drip nine drops on to the wart.

'The mowdy would be released and they thought that he took the infection underground with him, and that this would soon clear up the warts.'

'There is summat about moles in Grandad's book already,' Joe recalled reading about the car exhaust method and about caper spurge (see page 29). "So what about befriending hedgehogs?"

'I thought every gardener knew about hedgehogs?' said Seth.

'They don't,' Joe emphasised. 'So let's tell 'em.'

'Very useful animals to have in a garden, hedgehogs are,' Seth affirmed. 'In Yorkshire, we call 'em prickly-back urchins and they used to say they suckled cows at night, but I don't reckon that's possible. Even if a cow laid down, I doubt if the hedgehog's mouth would be big enough to cope with the cow's teats. But they do keep garden pests down, slugs, snails, beetles, woodlice, caterpillars and pests galore. So gardeners should attract 'em; try putting a plate of food out at night, some say tinned dog- or catfood. They're very tame, as you know; but I tell folks not to poison the pests, otherwise the hedgehog'll eat them and then die. And if you've a garden pond or there's a cattle grid nearby, put some wire netting up the sides so a hedgehog can climb out if it falls in. Then, in autumn, make somewhere for hedgehogs to hibernate. A dry corner with lots of leaves and grass will be fine, but make sure when you light your bonfires there's no hedgehogs inside.'

'You like hedgehogs, don't you?' Joe smiled.

'I do,' acknowledged Seth. 'Smashing little fellers, so I don't hold with gypsies baking 'em in mud; some said earache could be cured by rubbing in fat from a cooked hedgehog and I don't hold with that neither! And you can forecast the weather through hedgehogs. Listen to this old poem:

Observe the way the hedgehog builds her nest,
To front the north or south, or east or west;
For if it's true what common people say,
The wind will blow quite the contrary way!
If by some secret art, the hedgehog knows
So long before, which way the wind blows
She has an art which many a person lacks
That thinks himself fit to write almanacs!

'And,' Seth continued, 'they reckon hedgehogs will hide if there's going to be a change to a stormy wind. Some say they poke their noses out of hibernation on Candlemas Day, that's February 2nd, to see how the weather is. It's reckoned they know if the worst weather is over, in which case they'll come out. So if you see hedgehogs about in February or March it means a good spring, but that might also mean a poor summer!'

'Do other wild animals foretell the weather then?' Joe asked.

'Most of 'em can,' nodded Seth, draining his glass. He paused and Joe knew it would require a refill if Seth was to keep talking. He bought the drinks and Seth continued.

'Take rats,' he said. 'If rats are restless, you can bet there's rain on the way, and mice'll start squeaking and playing about when rain's due. Moles an' all – they'll dig more piles of soil before a rainstorm, and bats will cry and even fly into the house if they feel rain coming on. If a hare thinks it's going to snow, it will look for the open countryside so it's not hemmed in and squirrels seem to know when a severe winter's due, because they make a big store of nuts. Funny things, squirrels. They hide nuts and acorns in the ground all over the place, then forget where they put them! That way, we get lots of young hazel and oak trees. Funny thing, nature, how it survives.'

'You've told all this to Grandad, Seth?'

'Aye, and more. Well, Joe, I'd best be off. Thanks for the beer,' and he quickly drained his glass.

'I'll see what Grandad's written about the weather,' Joe assured him. 'And I might be back for more.'

'I talk better on a pint or two.' Seth grinned. 'It lubricates my old throat, you see!'

'I'll remember,' and Joe left for Emmerdale. Later that evening, he borrowed Grandad's notebook from Jack and turned to the section about the weather. He was pleased to see that many of Seth's contributions were included, but there were many others Grandad had entered, doubtless gleaned over the years from past and present residents of Beckindale.

THE WEEK AND THE WEATHER

One section contained old beliefs relating the days of the week to the weather and Grandad had written:

'There are many sayings about the days of the week. For example: if the sunset is cloudy on a Sunday, it will rain before Wednesday, or the last Sunday of any month indicates the weather for the next month. Another notion was that if there were storms on the first Sunday of a month, there'd be storms every Sunday that month. I could find nothing about Mondays and Tuesdays, but there is a saying that "Wednesday clearing, clear till Sunday", and another says that when the sun sets clear on a Wednesday, you can expect clear weather for the rest of the week.

'Some folk say you can forecast the weather by the time of day:

Thursday at three
Look out, and you'll see
What Friday will be!

'There are other sayings like that, such as "Rain at seven, fine before eleven; rain at eight, not fine till eight", and another one says "Between the hours of ten and two will show you what the day will do".

'So far as the days are concerned, Friday is thought to be either the fairest or the foulest day of the week and I've heard it said that if it's fine on Friday, it'll be fine on Sunday, but if it's wet on Friday, it will be wet on Sunday. If there's a clear sunset on Friday, there'll be wind before Sunday night and rain before Monday morning. The best is: "There's never a Saturday without some sunshine".

'On top of this, country folk know that every day tells its own future so far as the weather is concerned. Most of us know that a red sky at night is a shepherd's delight, meaning it'll be a fine day tomorrow, but a red sky in the morning is the shepherd's warning. If it's a misty morning (not foggy, but just a light mist), it's almost certain the rest of the day will be fine, but if the day has a very bright start, then it'll probably rain later. On those occasions in Yorkshire, we say "It's

ower glishy" – that means it's over bright or too bright, and it'll rain later. There was a saying in Shakespeare's time that "Too bright a morning brings a lowering day" (lowering means cloudy or stormy) and another belief is that if the grass is dry at first light, there'll be rain before night. Having said all that, we always reckon there'll be a spell of fair weather after rain!

'There's a very old guide and it goes like this: "If rain commences before daylight, it will hold up before 8am; if it begins about noon, it will continue through the afternoon; if it commences after 9pm, it will rain next day; if it clears off in the night, it will rain next day; if the wind is from the northwest or southwest, the storm will be short; if from the northeast, it will be a hard one; if from the northwest, a cold one and from the southwest a warm one. If it ceases after 12 midnight, it will rain next day; if it ceases before 12 midnight, it will be clear next day.

'If it begins about 5pm, it will rain through the night and if it is raining between 8 and 9am, it will go on till noon, and if it does not then cease, it will continue until evening.'

WEATHER AND WILDLIFE

'Still reading your Grandad's notes?' Annie brought a cup of coffee for Joe as he relaxed in the parlour.

'Aye,' he smiled. 'He's got a lot here about rain. I suppose we country folk worry a lot about rain or snow, but when your living depends on the state of the weather, it's important to learn what's in store. Now, listen to this, Ma,' and he read aloud, his voice sounding remarkably like that of his grandfather.

'I asked Seth if he could tell from the birds and wildlife if it was going to rain or be fine. He said there are lots of signs about forthcoming rain, such as sheep gathering in a sheltered corner or cows grouping together under trees, often with their backs to the wind; frogs making a lot of noise; pigs becoming unsettled and sometimes coating themselves in dust; moles being very active and digging lots of molehills or flies and midges biting hard!

'Birds can often tell when rain is coming: pigeons will come home to roost much later or more slowly than usual. The best rain forecasters are rooks; they've all sorts of ways of telling us when rain is coming. When they fall about in the sky, almost as if they've been shot, it's a sure sign of rain. They fly in tumbling motions – it's a curious sight. If they fly low across the land, that's another sign of rain, and also if they sit around their home area, or come back in the middle of the day instead of the evening.

'But if they hurry in their flight, or feed in a rush, then that indicates a storm; another sign of a storm is when rooks come to feed among the houses. In some parts of Yorkshire, they say that if rooks gather on the dead branches of a tree there'll be rain before nightfall, but if they use the living branches, then a fine day is forecast. On the other hand, rooks flying high and straight means fine weather and if they go far from home, again fine weather is due.

'Other members of the crow family, like carrion crows, ravens and jackdaws, will call loud and late if a storm's coming, and there's an old saying "The wicked crow aloud foul weather threats". Continuous cawing by a crow, or a kind of hiccup in its calls, means coming rain and perhaps wind. Some say that if crows go to the riverside or to a pond and take a bath by splashing themselves with their wings and shout a lot, then that indicates a storm. Pigeons and lots of other birds wash before rain, too, I'm told.'

Annie had settled in a chair to listen, and said, 'I was always told that if robins are seen near houses, then rain is coming but if they try to get into houses or buildings, then storms or snow and frost are forecast. If a robin sings for a long time and very loudly on a morning, it suggests rain, and in some parts of the country they say that if it's going to be stormy the robin will find a very high perch for his songs. In other parts, they say it'll be fine if he sings high!

'That's often true,' Joe agreed. 'Now, Grandad says,' and he read again:

'Two birds that are known for singing before rain are the green woodpecker and the missel thrush. Each calls a lot before rain or a storm; the green woodpecker is some-

times called the heigh-ho because of its laughing call, but it is also known as the yaffle, the popinjay or the rain bird. It is said to laugh in the sun because rain is coming. The missel thrush also sings before a storm or before rain, and usually selects a high place. It's often called the storm-cock for this reason. Sparrows and finches chirping a lot, especially chaffinches, and sometimes the call of an owl, will mean rain. Many old country folk say that owls calling at night mean a change in the weather and others say it means a fine day tomorrow.

'There's a good deal of weather lore about the cuckoo, too. If it calls from low-lying land, then rain is coming, but if it calls from high ground, fine weather can be expected. Some say that the cuckoo arrives just before spring storms and because some call this bird the gowk, the storms are known as gowk-storms. Generally, it's said that if a cuckoo sings from a bare hedge bad weather is on the way, but if it sings from a leafy hedge then fine weather is due.

'Swallows flying low and dipping into the surface of the water means rain, and so do starlings if they gather in large numbers.

'But there are other signs of fine weather, such as swallows and swifts flying high, bats flying later into the evening, insects and beetles flying in the evening and dew on the grass on a morning. One good old saying is that fair weather comes out of the north.'

FLOWER FORECASTS

'One of the best weather forecasters is the scarlet pimpernel,' Annie added. 'It's a very common flower, usually a bright red in colour, although you can get them in pink, white, blue and purple. You can find it straggling across the ground on lots of stalks and its tiny flowers are like small bright red stars with five petals.'

Joe added his knowledge. 'That was the pseudonym used by Sir Percy Blakeney in Baroness Orczy's stories of the French Revolution when he was known as "that damned elusive Pimpernel". Now Grandad's notes say: "In England, it is known as the ploughman's weather-glass, the shepherd's sundial or the poor man's weather-glass because it opens only for a short time – from sunrise until mid-afternoon – and it always closes when it is dull or raining. Country folk know that if the flowers do not open on a morning, then rain or bad weather is due that day. If they do open, then it is going to be fine."'

Enjoying these moments with her youngest son, Annie went on, 'Another plant does that, Joe. It's called either goat's beard or Jack-go-to-bed-at-noon. Its yellow flower is rather like a dandelion and its tall, thin leaves can be mistaken for grass.

'When it seeds, it produces a head of those downy little parachutes, just like a dandelion, but the flower opens only for a short time every day. It has usually closed into a narrow arrowhead shape by noon. It closes the flowers in damp weather an' all.'

'Lots of other wild flowers close their petals before it rains,' Joe added. 'One is the wood sorrel; at night, this also closes its flowers and its leaves, each with their three leaflets. Some call it the Sleeping Beauty, and because of its leaf-shape, some say this was the original shamrock used by St Patrick to illustrate the doctrine of the Holy Trinity, i.e. three in one. Others include varieties of sandwort, the ox-eye daisy, the germander speedwell or bird's-eye speedwell, tulips, convolvulus, African marigolds and the gentian.

'Now, let's see what else he's added.'

RAINBOWS AND MOONBOWS

Grandad's notes now contained a short section about rainbows and moonbows.

'Here in Yorkshire, it is said that "A dog at night is the farmer's delight", and there's a similar saying among sailors. "A dog in the morning, sailor take warning; a dog in the night is the sailor's delight". Now, a dog means a small rainbow or just part of one. Rainbows can be seen when the sun is behind a person who is looking at a rainfall; the sunlight is reflected and also refracted as it shines through the falling raindrops.

'This produces that lovely bow of colour. If you move towards it, it always moves away from you, and they say that if you could reach from you, and they say that if you could reach the end of a rainbow, you would find a pot of gold! Generally, if a rainbow, or part of one,

appears during the evening, it means it will rain but quickly fair up afterwards. A rainbow in the morning is usually an indication of rain that day. Another saying is that if a rainbow appears on a cloud that is approaching, showers are very likely, but if it appears on a cloud that is receding, then fine weather is a possibility. If a rainbow appears during a spell of fine weather, worse is to come, but if it makes an appearance during bad weather, then it will fair up. Some believe that if you see a rainbow over water, like a pond, lake or river, but it does not reach down to the water, then a fair day will follow.

'There is a bit of lore about the colours of a rainbow too. If blue shows strongest, it means the air is growing clearer, and if red and yellow are more clearly seen, we can expect a few days of fine weather. If green is showing clearly, it means continuing rain, and if green and blue predominate, then there will be rain the following night. If red is the strongest colour, it means wind and rain.

'There is a belief among some farmers that if a rainbow appears on a Saturday it heralds a week of bad weather, and that seven rainbows appearing one after another is a sign of eight days' rain!

'A rainbow that comes and goes very quickly is a sign of fine weather to follow next day and so is one which appears to be a long way off. Sometimes, when the sunlight is reflected twice instead of the usual once, there is a second bow outside the first one; this is usually paler in colour, but the colours are reversed. The order for a primary rainbow is red, orange, yellow, green, blue, indigo, violet.

'These are the colours of the spectrum and as children, we learned the sequence in the saying "Richard Of York Gains Battles In Vain". The initial letters are the initials of the rainbow colours, and it helps to memorise them.'

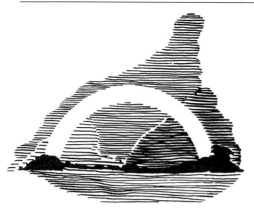

Grandad had added a short note to say that he had never seen a triple rainbow, although he had heard that these were occasionally seen, just as beautiful rainbows could occasionally be spotted in the spray at some of Yorkshire's waterfalls like Falling Foss, Aysgarth Falls and High Force in Teesdale.

THUNDERSTORMS

'In my young days,' Annie told Joe, 'it was always thought sensible that if you were out of doors and had to shelter in a thunderstorm, you should do so under an oak tree. We'd all been told that lightning will very rarely strike an oak tree, but on those rare occasions that it did, then the wood became a good luck charm against further strikes. The country folk would collect bits of any oak hit by lightning, and take them home as charms to keep their houses safe. People always thought that anything linked to the oak, such as acorns, oak apples and oak leaves, ensured good fortune as well as protection against lightning.'

'That's right,' Joe agreed, 'and for that reason, you'll find acorns carved in the woodwork of some houses and even in some churches. One of the favourite places in the home is at the tips of curtain rails, or those bobbins on strings which are used to pull down blinds. Even today, with modern plastic or brass curtain rails, you'll see representations of an acorn adorning the ends. It comes from an old idea that lightning would enter a house through the window, and so acorns were placed on window ledges to stop it. Later, any items linked to the decor of the window, such as curtain rails, pulls, etc., were adorned with acorns. Modern manufacturers may not realise they are perpetuating an ancient pre-Christian belief. To be honest, Ma, this superstition dates from pagan times. The oak was sacred to Thor, the god of thunder, and it was known as the thunder-tree or the abode of the Thunder God.

'The Druids thought it was sacred and then in the superstitious Middle Ages the people continued to think that the oak was in some way a magic tree. This mixture of superstition and paganism continued in the early days of Christianity and some young folks asked to be married under the oak or, after a church wedding, to have their union blessed under it! They thought it would bring happiness. Marriage Oaks and Gospel Oaks could be found in our countryside even in fairly recent times.'

'There's a verse we still say about oaks,' Annie recalled. 'It's this:

If the ash leaf is out before the oak
You may expect a thorough soak;
If the oak leaf is out before the ash
You'll hardly get a summer splash.

'It's pretty reliable and the verse comes in many different versions, but all say the same thing; that if the ash tree comes into leaf before the oak, we will have a wet summer or vice versa.'

'Grandad's got some more relating to other trees,' Joe said, reading from the notes. 'Listen:

"One very popular piece of lore is that the leaves of some trees turn their undersides uppermost before rain is due. Now, we all know that, and it's a sure sign of rain: 'When the leaves show their undersides/Be very sure that rain betides'. 'The sycamore, poplar, aspen, silver maple and lime are all good examples.

'"A very general rule is that if a tree bears lots of berries or fruit, then a hard winter is expected. This is nature's way of feeding the birds and animals such as squirrels. Holly trees, mountain ash, hawthorns, oaks and beech are good examples."'

'We used pine cones,' Annie said, 'They're good at forecasting the weather too. If you hang them in the house, they will close when it is wet and open when it is dry and warm; seaweed hanging outside a house also turns wet and soft if it's going to rain, and dries when the weather is fine.'

HARES

'Hello,' said Joe, separating two pages of the notebook. He had found a note in Seth's handwriting. 'There's one thing me and other keepers keep getting asked,' Seth had written. 'It's about mad March hares. Folks ask if they're really mad, so I thought I'd send this note for your book.

'In March, hares do daft things; they balance on their hind legs and box one another with their forelegs. It looks just like a fight. The ears flop back, then suddenly one will stop fighting and run round in a circle with the other chasing. Then they stop and box a bit more, sometimes leaping into the air and lashing out with their hind legs.

'You can often see lots of them in one field, all boxing like this; then, for no

apparent reason, they'll all stop and sit around as if thinking about something. One or two might rear up to peer around the place while others lie very still, just like lumps of earth. Then they'll set off again, with more boxing.

'But they're not mad. It used to be thought these were two jacks putting on a display to win the affections of a doe, but it's more likely to be a doe resisting the desires of a jack. But when all this palaver is over, she will select her mate. The leverets are born in May, with their eyes wide open, but the jack doesn't look after them. He goes off to live alone but next March he might return for another fight with a potential mate. The doe is the bigger of the pair, you see, and she usually gives him a rough time. That's love for you! A bit like me and our Meg...'

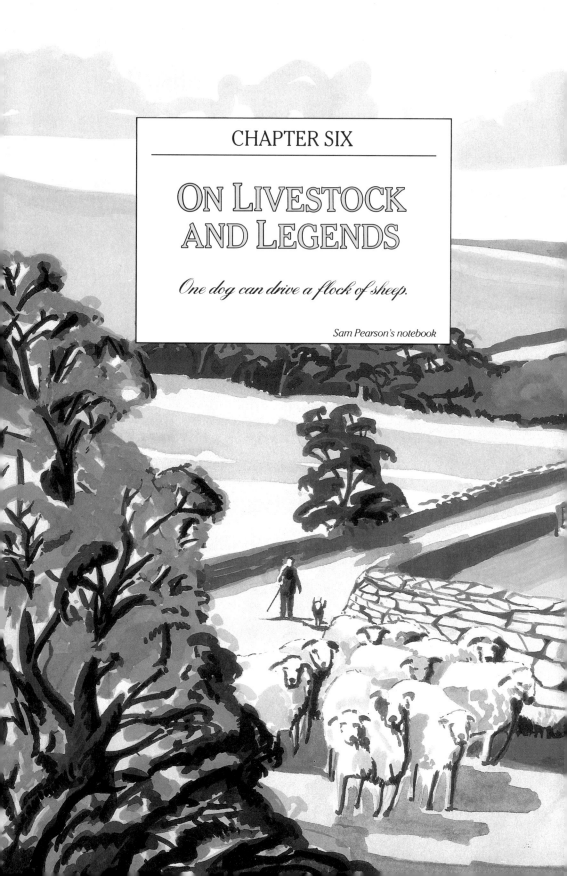

CHAPTER SIX

ON LIVESTOCK AND LEGENDS

One dog can drive a flock of sheep.

Sam Pearson's notebook

Matt and Jack were on Leck Fell enjoying a few moments' rest after rounding up the moorland sheep. The animals had undergone one of their quarterly counts and happily none was missing. All seemed in good health, so it had been a satisfactory morning's work. Now that the task was over the men were chatting as they leaned upon a dry-stone wall, the enduring product of an anonymous dalesman's labours some two hundred years ago.

'Built to last, these walls were,' commented Jack. 'Simple but effective, eh? It amazes me how they managed to build them in such difficult places, on the tops of crags and down hillsides that are too steep for roads.'

'Aye,' Matt agreed. 'There's an art in building a good wall. There's no mortar to bind the stones – they fit into each other like a jigsaw and never shift for years. It's all done by hand; wallers use their eyes for measuring up, yet these stones have stood up to all manner of weathers, right down the years. They enclose our land, shelter the stock and provide homes for little animals and birds. See those gaps between the stones? They let air in which keeps the damp at bay; they go deep inside and are as dry as toast so birds, mice and voles will make nests in there. Safe and cosy for all, eh? See how the tops are narrower than the bottoms, to help the water drain off? And those long stones called "throughs" which pass through to bind it all together?'

'I like the patterns they make on the slopes of the Dales, Matt.'

'The first walls were a bit haphazard,' Matt said. 'You can still see fields and enclosures in weird shapes, but about the turn of the 18th century, when the Enclosure Acts came into force, walls became longer and straighter. Farmers preferred them to hedges and fences because they last longer, cost less to maintain and give more shelter.'

'What I like,' smiled Jack, 'is the variety of stiles that cross 'em. Have a look some time – there's V stiles, for example, usually fashioned from stone. They're wide at the top but narrow below, so men and dogs can get through but not horses or cattle; then there's the zig-zag which has a weighted gate in a Y formation. This blocks the way for animals but lets humans through. Hereabouts, we call 'em kissing gates! On the moors where sheep roam around walled areas, special holes are constructed at ground level so that they can pass through. They are called smouts or smoutholes. If a large stone is used to temporarily block the smout, it's called a smoutstone, or smowtsteean. "Smowt" means to crawl!

'Now, on the big country estates, or those where there's dykes to cross, they usually have ladder stiles with a handrail which makes them safe when carrying guns. Some stiles are built into walls by incorporating large flat stones at angles, like steps – there's a lot of those in the slate walls of the Lake District – then there's turnstiles and Cornish slabs.

'Turnstiles were simply a cross on a swivelling post, and they've been copied and mechanised at zoos, football grounds, parks and even public toilets. They've even copied Cornish slabs, you know; these were long narrow slabs of stone set lengthways across a gap or a footpath. I think even they were copied from similar ideas used by the Romans! The stones protruded from the ground, making deep ruts between each one, and cloven-hoofed animals didn't like to cross them. The modern version of these Cornish slabs is the cattle grid, parallel bars of metal over a deep trough instead of a gate. Cloven-hoofed animals won't cross those!'

'There's a lot to see for them that's got eyes to look,' said Matt. 'Well, Jack, it's dinner time. Let's get back.'

Matt Skilbeck

COUNTING SHEEP

As they walked to the farmhouse for their midday meal, Jack said, 'Matt, when you counted the sheep, did you use that old Yorkshire method?'

'Yan, tan, tethera, you mean? No, I've never learned it properly. My grandad used it, but I never have. Do you know it?'

'I sometimes use it, but not aloud.'

'You know it then?'

'When I was in Rome, I discovered the Greek way of counting and realised it was very like the Yorkshire one, so I memorised both. Now, this is the modern Greek – listen: Ena, Theeo, Treea, Tessera, Pende, Exi, Efta, Okto, Ennea, Thekka.

'The ancient Greek was Hen, Duo, Treis, Tessares, Pente, Hex, Hepta, Octo, Ennea, Dekem. Now here in North Yorkshire, the older shepherds would count the sheep like this: Ena, Tena, Tethera, Pethera, Pimps, Saffra, Lafra, Ofra, Dofra, Dix.'

'When we were kids,' Matt grinned, 'we played a game that started Ena, Mena, Mina, Mo! But how did they count sheep if there were more than ten?'

'In the Dales, the shepherds counted from eleven to twenty like this: Ena Dix, Tena Dix, Tethera Dix, Pethera Dix, Bumpit, Ena Bumpit, Tena Bumpit, Tethera Bumpit, Pethera Bumpit, Siggit. Then twenty-one was Ena Siggit, twenty-two was Tena Siggit and so on, with thirty being Tiggit, but few, if any, counted higher than thirty in this way. There were slight variations between the Dales and other parts of England such as the Lake District or County Durham; in Nidderdale, for example, it would be Yain, Tain, Eddero, Peddero, Pitts, Tayter, Later, Overro, Coverro, Dix, while over in Swaledale, it would be Yahn, Tayhn, Tether, Mether, Mimph, Hither, Lither, Anver, Danver, Dic. There'd be differences between the North York Moors and the Craven district and Wensleydale. The counting was usually done in a kind of rhythm, almost musical, and if you compare other tongues, such as Sanskrit, Welsh, Romany, Cornish and Gaelic, you'll see similarities.'

'If I had to count like that, I'd never be done!' Matt chuckled. 'There's another thing I've found when I'm visiting places away from here, towns especially. They don't know what we mean by calling our sheep hoggs, gimmers, tups, mules, wedders or wethers, and heeaft ewes.'

'I'll bet you don't know builders' jargon either, or sea fishermen's sayings! So go on, tell me what you mean by those sheep names. What's a hogg, with two g's?'

'While he's still suckling at the ewe, a young male sheep is known as the tup-lamb or even a pur-lamb. When he's taken from the ewe, he's called a hogg-tup, a hogg, a hoggett, a lamb-hogg, a gimmer-hogg or a teg, depending where you live! A hogg, therefore, is a young male sheep before its first shearing. It is shorn when it's about eighteen months old, and it is then a shearling hogg. When it's an adult, it is a ram, sometimes called a tup in Yorkshire, and pronounced teeap in the local dialect. When it's been shorn twice, it's a two-shear ram and so on. If it is castrated while still suckling from its mother, it is a wedder or wether lamb. A gimmer is a young female sheep who is still suckling, and she is sometimes called a gimmer-lamb or gimmer-ewe. This is before she becomes adult. After her first shearing, she becomes a shearling ewe or sometimes just a gimmer. She can be a two-shear ewe, a four-shear ewe and so forth. It's when she's an adult that she is just a ewe – which is pronounced yow in Yorkshire. Old ewes are sometimes called crones or drapes!

'On the North York Moors, old ewes are often called rannocks. Now, a heeaft yow (a heaft or heft ewe) is a female sheep who lives on the open moor. Sheep have got an instinct to remain in the area where they were reared; this is called a heaf or a heft. Once a sheep settles in that area, we say she's heft or heeaft, which means she's at home – and she'll not stray even though there's no fences. And a mule? Well, Jack, that's a cross-bred sheep.'

'So you know your stuff!' laughed Jack. 'But we all mark our sheep with distinctive dyes or horn markings, or we clip their ears, just to make it easier to identify those which do stray or get lost. My dad used to put a bell on the neck of a wedder, calling it the bell-wedder, or he'd do so on an old ewe. It was usually a leader of the flock, and where it went the others followed; in fog, you could always tell where the flock was. If the bell rang rapidly, it could mean the flock was in trouble, being chased by dogs mebbe. Sheep always follow their leader – I remember some slaughtermen would have a Judas sheep; she was kept to lead the others into the slaughter-house.'

'It's a cruel world, Jack, but those markings you mention can puzzle visitors and tourists. Some can't understand why sheep are wandering about with red or blue patches on their shoulders or backsides! It's a good way of claiming ownership. Tell you what, though, Jack, you never see a pinfold in use these days, do you? For holding animals, for counting them even or containing strays.'

Jack agreed and thought back to his younger days. Pinfolds were not widely used then, although many Dales villages boasted one – and still do, although some are called pounds. They were small enclosures built of stone, sometimes round and sometimes square-shaped, with a gate or entrance at one side. Their original purpose was to contain livestock which had been found straying in the village, or on the lanes and byways. You might come across cows, sheep, horses, donkeys, pigs or even goats inside, and the maintenance of the pinfold was the job of a pinder, a man appointed by the parish council or court leet. He had to make sure the owners, when found, paid for the keep of their animals and also that none of them tried to sneak their stock out of the pinfold without paying! That was known as Pound Breach and was a criminal offence.

'They weren't a bad idea,' said Jack. 'At least there was somewhere to put a stray animal if you couldn't find the owner. It's better than pushing it into the nearest field – I've known fine pedigree herds be contaminated by stray animals being shoved into fields to roam among them.'

'The pinfolds I've seen are used as little gardens, some with seats in them!' smiled Matt. 'Mind, I think if I found a stray beast and didn't know what to do with him, I'd still push him into a pinfold if I could find one! If he ate the flowers, it would remind officialdom what those little enclosures are really for!'

'I'd do that, an' all,' agreed Jack.

WEATHER FORECASTING

As the two men walked in a moment of silence, Matt suddenly halted and turned to Jack.

'Jack,' he asked, 'did Grandad ever talk to you about this sort of thing? You know, country ways and sayings.'

'He didn't ask me much,' Jack admitted. 'But he did leave me an old notebook among some other odds and ends. I don't know what he expected me to do with it, but it's full of old sayings, weather lore, bits and pieces on country life and so on.'

'You reminded me of him just now,' Matt smiled. 'He kept asking me things like this, for some notes.'

'Well, I've got those notes, Matt, and I'm trying to knock them into some kind of order.'

'Are you going to publish them, then? Your next book?'

'I'll see how I get on with them, Matt. So what sort of things did he ask you?'

'Well, all sorts really, over a long period of time. Things about shepherding, farm animals, some wild animals I might come across. Weather sayings that farmers use.'

'Come on, Matt! You must remember some of the things you told him!'

Matt pondered in silence as they resumed their walk and then said, 'Aye, I told him about not shearing sheep too early – there's a saying that if you shear your sheep in May, you shear them all away. Best to wait till later, July or August even. And another thing is to keep caring for them – just one sheep with scab will ruin the whole flock.'

'And what about sheep being able to forecast bad weather?'

'Oh, well, everybody knows they can!'

'Not *everybody* knows, Matt! So what did you tell him?'

'Well, it's well known among country folk that moor sheep will come down from the hills, and make a lot of bleating noise, when bad weather's on the way. They always leave high ground before a storm, but if they seem to be reluctant about it, then rain's coming.'

'Anything else?' asked Jack.

'If they stand with their backs to the wind, and stay like that for a long time, then that means rain and windy weather is due. You'll find it's usually the older sheep that do that. If we're to get more than rain, then the younger sheep tend to get a bit frisky. They start playing about, jumping up and down, butting each other in fun, that sort of thing. That's a sign of storms or a change in the weather – for the worse.'

'What about their feeding habits? An old chap told me years ago that you can tell the coming weather by the way a sheep eats.'

'I wouldn't be too sure about that,' answered Matt. 'I know they say a sheep'll eat sparingly before a thaw sets in, and if they start to eat uphill, then fair weather is coming. In winter, when they eat downhill, snow's on the way – so they say!'

'I've heard it said,' Jack added, 'that some sheep'll become very greedy before a storm, eating like gluttons, and that some will even fight others to get food before a storm sets in.'

'Aye, funny things, animals,' said Matt. 'They know more than we think. Talking of feeding, sheep can survive under snow for weeks without food. Their wool keeps 'em warm and they eat the snow for moisture, their own fat keeping 'em alive. They make a sort of igloo around themselves in deep drifts and so long as they can breathe, they're OK.'

'I remember we've had some remarkable discoveries on these fells in a tough winter,' Jack agreed. 'We've dug sheep out alive weeks after they've been lost. Up in Scotland somewhere, in 1978, a chap dug a sheep out alive after it had been buried 50 days. That's very nearly two months!

'That reminds me of another thing,' said Jack. 'Sheep trods. The paths they've created over mebbe hundreds of years, sheep tracks. Trods we call them. I was told years ago by Grandad that if I ever got lost on the moors, especially if a fog suddenly came down, then I could reach safety by following a sheep trod. They all lead to lower ground and if bad weather is due, the sheep can usually get down to safety in time. But not always, eh?'

'No, some get stuck, but they're hardy survivors, are moorland sheep.'

'They've got to be!' grinned Jack. 'It's a tough life!'

'In fact,' continued Matt, 'it's because they seem to survive most things that folks used to think they were charmed and able to help humans overcome diseases. When people were ill or off-colour, some would be told to sleep among a flock of sheep, or to lie on a place where a sheep had slept.'

'That idea of them being charmed comes from their links with the Nativity of Christ,' said Jack. 'Lambs feature a lot in the Christian religion and the lamb is the emblem of Christ. Christ was known as the Lamb of God, and in some continental countries lamb was eaten as an Easter dish. And one was said to be present in the stable during the birth of Christ. That's why some think meeting a flock of sheep brings good luck, or even meeting a single lamb, especially if it's the first of the spring and it's facing towards you! They do say, you know, that all sheep turn to the east and bow to their knees at midnight of Christmas Eve in memory of their very important role that night. But they do it in secret, so nobody'll ever see them!'

'That's one way of keeping a rumour circulating!' laughed Matt. 'Now, Jack, this book of Grandad's. Does it say owt about pigs being able to see the wind?'

'It does, and I can tell you what he's written. He's included that tale about pigs being able to see the wind, but says it might not be true. One thing is certain, though, and it's that pigs do become very unsettled and even frightened when the wind's getting up.'

Matt nodded. 'It certainly upsets them.'

'I've seen 'em disturbed in windy weather,' Jack continued. 'Years ago this made country folk think that the pig, of all the animals, could actually see the wind. The people thought it must be a very frightening thing to see. Another thing is that if pigs rub themselves against posts and walls, then that's supposed to mean there's a thaw on the way. And Grandad has a note that some

pigs would pick up bits of hay and straw and run round with them in their mouths before a storm. He's added a little verse that goes: "When pigs carry sticks/The clouds will play tricks/When they lie in the mud/No fears of a flood."'

Matt smiled. 'Aye, I remember him asking me about that; then he went on about pigs bringing bad luck to brides.'

'That's right. If a pig crossed the path of a bride on her way to church or coming back from her wedding, then it was a sign of bad luck. I know a lot of seamen, fishermen especially, won't use the word "pig" on board ship and reckon it's unlucky to meet a pig while travelling to their boats. If that happens, they'd rather turn back than go to sea.'

Matt nodded – he'd come across that belief during some of his holidays at Bridlington – then he said, 'Grandad was telling me about pig-killing days. Nearly every cottager in a village kept a pig or two, to see them through the winter in food.'

'That was in the days of self-sufficiency,' said Jack.

'Aye, folks had to fend for themselves and plan ahead. They had pig-killing days, and it was always reckoned bad luck to kill pigs on

Mondays because the meat could not be cured; it wouldn't take the salt. There was another tale that you should always kill pigs when the moon is waxing, otherwise you couldn't cure the meat. It wouldn't "take salt" either, and some still believe that!'

THE FAMILY PIG

Matt's reference to pig-killing days revived a host of memories for Jack. Each year, in either late November or early December, depending upon whether the moon was waxing or waning, he could recall intense activity outside around the pig creels and scalding tubs. In fact, any month with an 'R' in it was regarded as suitable for pig-killing. In the kitchen, his mother and other helpers would prepare for their part. After the pig was humanely killed and bled, its carcass was scalded and scraped (often with the bases of old tin candlesticks) to remove the hair, and then it was cut up. Large pieces of white fat were diced into small pieces and the women placed these in trays in very hot ovens where they were rendered down into fat. The liquid fat became lard, while the surplus pieces were known as scrappings. These were very tasty and were eaten by everyone as a treat, sometimes alone or sometimes with bread and salt.

The meat was cut into selected pieces such as spare rib or fillets, while the large pieces were cured. The hams, shoulders and sides were salted and kept in the salt for some three weeks. Then they were hung from hooks in the kitchen ceiling – lots of farmhouses, country houses and cottages still have those large hooks in the beams – and, when the hanging meat was dry, pieces would be cut from it as and when required. The quantity cured and hung in the house depended upon the size of the family, but it would last throughout the winter.

The smaller pieces of meat were never thrown out. Pork pies were made from some of it, and brawn was made from the odds and ends which had no particular value, like the feet, tail and head, sometimes with items from other animals added. Jack had found a very old recipe for brawn among Grandad's notes.

Although he had not eaten brawn for years, Jack could recall the other pig-cheer that was distributed at pig-killing. This comprised cuttings from the various parts, such as bacon, and was given to friends and neighbours to celebrate a pig-killing, or to thank those who had helped. There used to be a superstition that the dish containing bits of pig-cheer had to be returned unwashed otherwise the new meat would not be successfully cured. The pig-cheer was then cooked and eaten as a savoury meal with sage, onions and apple sauce.

Every piece of a pig was used for something; even the bladder was kept and blown up to hold lard or for use as a football! An old saying went, 'On pig-killing day, nothing is wasted except the squeak.'

One other delicacy eaten at this time was the pig-killing cake. This was about half an inch thick. It was made from 1 lb flour, 3 or 4 oz lard, currants to taste, a pinch of salt, sugar to taste, a teaspoonful of baking powder and some milk or cream, around half a cupful. It was baked in a big frying pan covered with a lid and turned carefully after about 5 minutes. It was then cut into small cakes, rather like scones, which were a welcoming delicacy for all manner of celebrations. Without the currants and sugar, they were called mell-cakes, turf cakes or bakestone cakes, depending upon the occasion. They were delicious if they were made over a peat fire with the flavour of the moors in them, then split and eaten hot with a covering of real butter!

'You've gone quiet, Jack!' remarked Matt as they approached Emmerdale farmhouse.

'I was thinking about food!' grinned Jack.

HOW THEY USED TO MAKE BRAWN

Take the head and piece of the belly of a young porker and rub it well with saltpetre. Let it lie three days and wash it. Split the head and boil it. Remove any bones and cut it into pieces. Take four ox feet boiled tender, cut into thin pieces and lay them in the belly piece with the head cut small. The pig's head and the feet (which can be from a pig, ox, cow or sheep) are necessary because of the gelatine produced by the bones; this sets the brawn. Roll up tight with sheet tin and boil for four or five hours. Then sit on end and put a trencher on it within the tin, press it down with a large weight and let it stand all night. Next morning, take it out of the tin, bind it with a fillet, put into cold salt water, and it is fit for use.

'I hope Ma's got a good dinner ready.'

'She will have. Talking of food and pigs, you'll know what a wreckling is?'

'Aye, a little pig, the smallest of a litter. Usually, the poor little blighter can't compete with his brothers and sisters for food, or he gets laid on by his careless mother and he's generally left out of things. Some don't survive, or else they're taken into the care of the farm family and reared safely.'

'Aye, and in Scotland it's called a sharger, while other names include pipment, parson's pig, tail-ender, runt, or tantony (which comes from St Anthony's pigs).'

As they approached the farmhouse, the scent of a welcoming hot meal wafted across to them. 'I'll not be a wreckling this dinner time!' laughed Jack. 'See you later.'

'Aye,' and Matt turned towards his own cottage and Dolly. 'Can I have a look at that book of Grandad's?'

'Sure,' said Jack, wondering whether pork was on today's menu.

ON COWS AND BULLS

That night, when Dolly was babysitting for Jock and Liz MacDonald, Matt occupied himself by dipping into Grandad's comprehensive notebook of country lore. His interest was first attracted by a section dealing with cows and bulls.

'There is a story that cows have sweet breath because they used it to warm the baby Jesus in the stable at Bethlehem and, years ago, country folk would make cows breathe on them if they had consumption,' he read. 'It was thought to be a cure. Cow dung was often used as a method of healing open cuts and wounds, too, or even to cure a headache!

'The countryman always thought a lot about his cows, especially the calves they produced, for they were all so important to him. In the North Riding of Yorkshire, there was a ritual involving an aborted calf. The little dead animal was either buried under the entrance to the cowshed, so that every incoming cow would step across it, or the skin was nailed to the wall so that every cow would look at it. It was thought that this would make sure the cows looked after themselves to avoid losing their offspring, and that if there were any evil spirits in the dead calf, they would be destroyed as the carcass rotted.

'When a calf was born, no one should step over it because this would endanger its life, and in some areas it was thought unlucky for a new-born calf if a human touched it with bare hands, so gloves should be worn to handle it. A fairly general notion in Yorkshire is that if twin calves are born, the first will be strong and fertile, while the second will be infertile. To counteract this, the infertile animal should be mated with a bull or cow who was also the second-born of twins.

'Milk and butter is open to superstition too. Some say that thunder makes milk turn sour, and in olden days farmers would place a poker or iron rod across the tops of buckets of milk, so that it would not be harmed by the thunder. One very widespread belief on farms was that no one should spill milk, because the fairies would invade the house to lap it up!

'In the days when farmers made their own butter and took it to market, it was an important part of the farm income. Consequently, successful butter-making was vital to any farm and if, for any reason, the milk in the hand-operated churn refused to "come" into butter, it was thought to be the work of a mischievous evil spirit. That spirit had therefore to be kept at bay!

'In North Yorkshire, there was a verse which served as a charm against these imps – it was:

Come butter come
Come butter come;
Peter stands at the gate
Waiting for a butter cake
So come butter come.

'Perhaps it was thought that mention of St Peter's name would frighten off anything connected with the Devil. There are variations of this charm in other parts of the country. One charm was to toss salt on to the fire before churning, and another was to dip a red-hot poker in the milk to frighten off evil spirits – it usually worked!

'One old idea was that the best milk for butter-making came from cows that had eaten grass from a churchyard, while some would toss a silver coin into the churn to make the butter come.

'So far as the weather is concerned, it's said that if cattle lie down during a shower, then it will become fair again quite soon, and if they go up to the hilltops, then fine weather is ensured. A very old piece of lore said that before rain, snow, hail, thunder or lightning, a cow would thrash her tail against a hedge or a wall, or even against her own body, or sometimes try to scratch her ear with her hind leg. If a cow's milk yield is reduced, stormy, cold weather is coming; you can usually tell when it's going to rain because the cows will stop walking and will shake their heads a lot, or group together, or refuse to go into their normal pastures. Other things to look for when rain is coming include the cows making a lot of lowing noises, looking up at the sky and sniffing, licking their own front feet, rubbing against things or lying down early in the day. If a cow holds her tail aloft or twists it into a funny shape, then that's also reckoned to be a sign of showers.

'Now, when bulls lick their hooves or lie on their right side, rain is coming, and they'll sometimes turn their backs to the wind or lick themselves against the lie of their hair for the same reason. There is a belief that lightning will never strike a bull, and in a thunderstorm, some farmers would join the bull in its stall for shelter.'

THE LEGEND OF THE DEAD DONKEY

'One of the legends of the Dales is that no one has ever seen a dead donkey. If you ask folks if they have seen one, you'll get a negative answer. In Beckindale, there was a farmer who took donkeys in during the winter, when they were resting after a summer on the beach at Bridlington and Scarborough. A tale got around that one had died, and that it was lying under a heap of sacks in the farmer's barn. Now, it's often said to mean good luck if you see a dead donkey, so dozens of folks from miles around trekked to see this one. Sure enough, it was lying very still under the sacks and the people just stood around, looking at it.

'Anyway, it seems somebody had called the owner all the way from Scarborough and he turned up with a patent pill of some sort. He pushed it down the donkey's throat and after half-an-hour it was galloping around like a young 'un. So we still haven't seen a dead donkey in Beckindale.

'While on the subject of donkeys, the braying of a donkey is said to herald rain, and farmers say: "When the donkey starts to bray, it's time to cock your corn and hay." The truth is, if a donkey brays, he's just letting other donkeys know he's there!

'Legend says the black cross on a donkey's back is because this animal carried Christ into Jerusalem on Palm Sunday, and an old cure for whooping cough was to pass the sufferer nine times under the belly of a donkey. Some thought that cross had curative powers.'

THE HORSEMAN'S WORD

'One of the greatest mysteries of the countryside is the Horseman's Word. For years, certain people who work with horses, such as grooms, ploughmen and blacksmiths, have had complete power over horses just by whispering a certain Word. It is so strong a word that it will halt a galloping horse or tame a wild stallion; it will make a horse follow the man until he tells it to stop, and it will obey that man without question.

'The Word is known only to a few people, and it is passed along in circumstances of great secrecy. Now there are fewer horses who work on our farms, this Word is seldom used and so the secret may die out. But there are many stories of uncontrollable horses being tamed by a man whispering the Word to them. It's a well-kept secret.'

ON HORSES AND HORSE BRASSES

'You often see horse brasses in public houses and gift shops. These are mostly no more than ornaments – especially now when they use them on horses at shows and ceremonies – but the originals were to protect the horse against the evil eye and witchcraft. The brasses were decorated with emblems which kept evil at bay, but a horse rarely wore a full set. It might wear one each day on its collar or harness, and a full set for special occasions. They were beautifully made of solid brass, proper craftsmanship – not like modern copies – and were handed down from father to son as a valuable heirloom. Some original ones are still around but most of them are lost and cheap imitations are being sold as trinkets.

'So far as horses are concerned, there is still a belief that a horse with four white socks is unlucky, while one with just one white sock is lucky:

If you have a horse with four white legs
Keep him not a day;
If you have a horse with three white legs
Send him far away;
If you have a horse with two white legs
Sell him to a friend;
And if you have a horse with one white leg
Keep him to the end.

'There's many sayings about horses, for example: a secretive man is said to be a dark horse; you shouldn't look a gift horse in the mouth (that means you shouldn't inspect gifts too closely – you could always tell a horse's age by looking at its teeth and if a horse was a gift, you might receive an unpleasant shock!). Also, when told something "straight from the horse's mouth", it means it's the truth; a horse's mouth never lies about the age of that horse. A favourite saying these days is that somebody has locked the stable door when the horse has bolted. He's learned his lesson too late. There's lots more sayings about horses, too many for my notebook, but if I've favourites, it's these: "A horse is neither better nor worse for his trappings" and "Better ride a donkey that will carry you than a horse that will throw you!"

'By the way, the best place for storing apples when they've been picked in the autumn is in the loft above a stable. The horses below produce just the right temperature for keeping the apples in the best of condition – provided they've no bruises or badness in them when they're put down for storing. They are best wrapped in straw or sawdust and separated from one another so none touches a neighbour. Under the beds in farmhouse bedrooms used to be a very suitable place, too, but that's no good in centrally-heated houses. It's too dry. A stable occupied by horses is still as good as anywhere.'

ON DOGS AND CATS

'I could fill a book about cats. To the ancient Egyptians they were sacred animals and here in Yorkshire they were always regarded as witches' animals – some thought a witch could turn herself into a cat. Nowadays, though, a black cat is thought to be a sign of good luck if it crosses your path or comes into the house, although some say you must stroke it three times for the luck to come. Some think it's lucky to own a black cat, but it used to be said that if any cat leaves the house when someone is ill, then it means that person will die. If a house-cat sneezes close to a bride on her wedding-day, she'll have a good marriage, but if it sneezes any other time, it means rain!

'One odd belief that still prevails is that May kittens are unlucky. Lots of people would drown kittens born in May simply because they'd been born in that month; they thought they would be ill, weak or no use about the farm. Worse still, some thought May kittens would kill babies by lying on their faces in cots and prams, but all this nonsense goes back to the days when country folk thought cats were in league with witches, and that witches did their worst evils during May!

'So far as dogs are concerned, country folk say that if a dog eats grass or rolls in dust or dirt then rain is coming, while a howling dog is the sign of a storm. If a dog howled near the home of a sick person, it was thought to indicate a death in the near future and there's a fairly strong suggestion, even now, that a dog can see a ghost. There are lots of tales about dogs refusing to enter certain haunted rooms or places where ghosts are reputed to appear.

'And so far as I'm concerned, there's no truth in the saying that a dog grows to look and behave like its master or mistress!'

SOME FARM SAYINGS

'He that buys land also buys the stones.
'A ploughman standing up is higher than a king kneeling.
'It's a poor sack that can't be mended.
'Rich soil left uncultivated produces strong weeds.
'A farmer's care makes a field bear.'

CHAPTER SEVEN

ON BIRTHS
AND BAIRNS

*Choose your wife as you would want
your children to be.*

Sam Pearson's notebook

S o that Annie could enjoy a day's outing to Hotten, Dolly was looking after Jack's baby son, Robert, and she had also cooked the dinner. The men had eaten the meal with undisguised pleasure and she was now washing the pots. They had all returned to their work in the fields and buildings except Jack; he had some paperwork to complete which had to catch that evening's post. He worked quietly on his papers while Dolly completed her work.

'Well, that's it,' he said eventually. 'So how about a cup of tea before I get back to my outside chores?'

'No sooner said than done!' she smiled. 'I'm ready for one an' all; the others'll be in for theirs later.'

As Jack settled down to his early tea-break, she asked, 'Jack, Matt said summat about a book of Grandad's. You're thinking of publishing it, he said?'

'Grandad left it to me,' Jack told her. 'I'm not sure whether he wanted it published, but I've been going through it to see just how complete it is. It seems Grandad had chatted to most folks hereabouts, asking them questions.'

'Aye, well, he did ask me, but I never got around to telling him everything. I did tell him bits and pieces, but I made more notes – they're in my dressing table drawer.'

'Really? What sort of things did he ask you?' Jack couldn't visualise Dolly knowing about the weather or bygone customs and folklore.

'He mentioned it just before his death, Jack, but he died before I got my notes finished. He was interested in children's games and local rhymes that children sing. They still enjoy that sort of thing in playschool, you see, or in the playground at the Beckindale primary school. I went around the mums and even grandmothers, and got them to delve into their memories for me.'

'That's great!' Jack enthused. 'Hang on, I'll get Grandad's notebook now, and see just what he has included about children.'

'And I'll pop home to get my notes!

ON BIRTH

Grandad's notebook contained an incomplete section about children, love, romance and weddings. He had scribbled a little note to say that Dolly was gathering more information for him.

'Right, Dolly,' Jack said. 'I can spare the time right now. How about you?'

'Fine, little Sam's at school and your Robert is asleep, so I've a few minutes. I'm dying to see what he's written down.'

Grandad's notes began: 'In my young days and well into the 20th century, country folk believed that a child's date and time of birth was of importance to his or her future. For centuries, it had been believed that the day of birth indicated something of the character of the child, and this famous old verse continues that wisdom:

> Monday's child is fair of face,
> Tuesday's child is full of grace,
> Wednesday's child is full of woe
> And Thursday's child has far to go.
> Friday's child is loving and giving,
> And Saturday's child works hard for his living;
> But the child that is born on the Sabbath day
> Is blithe and bonny, good and gay.

'It was believed that Sunday was the best day to be born because the Devil and his evil spirits had so little influence during that day. In some cases, it was thought that children born on Sundays had second-sight and that they could see ghosts. Another good day to be born was Christmas Day because this was when Christ was born, and therefore a fine future lay in store for any person lucky enough to share His birthday.

Dolly Skilbeck

'There are variations on this verse; they include versions that a Monday child is full in the face, a Tuesday child is solemn and sad, a Wednesday child is merry and glad and a Thursday child is inclined to thieving! Some verses suggest that a Friday child is born to sorrow, but all hint that a Sunday birth is a fortunate one, thus ensuring the child will be both lucky and generous throughout life.

'Of the months of the year, May was often thought to be the unluckiest to be born in, for children as well as animals, because this was when the witches were at their most evil and active! Those born in May were often considered unlikely to mature or to lead a full, healthy life.

'Another factor which was thought to affect a child was the precise time of its birth. Those born within the hour following midnight were the most fortunate, being blessed with high intelligence, health, happiness and the possession of second-sight. In some areas, it was thought beneficial to be born during the chime-hours; these were literally the times the local church clock chimed. This was not always on every hour; sometimes it was on the hours of three, six, nine and twelve, or four, eight and twelve.

'There is another old and much-quoted saying that "the later the hour, the shorter the life". This means it is better to be born early in the morning if you desire a long life; furthermore, to be born around sunrise often indicates a future life blessed with intelligence and success, whereas birth at sunset suggests a life of idleness and no ambition.

'On the Yorkshire coast, it was thought a good omen if a child was born as the tide came in, but a bad one if the tide was going out. The moon was also believed to affect births, there being an increase in the number of births as the moon was changing or just before a new moon. There was a general idea that any child born under a waning moon would be unlucky.

'At the birth, the new baby was given a gift to ensure a lucky and happy future; this was usually a piece of silver or a coin, but some of the gifts were reminders of pagan times, such as salt, garlic, a piece of iron or even a cross fashioned from the wood of a rowan tree. Even now, some are given a rabbit's foot for luck; another idea was to take the child up to the highest point of the house before taking it downstairs. It was thought important that a new child should go up in the world before going down! Often, when a birth was at home, the mother's room was the highest in the house and this presented problems, so a chair would be placed near the door. The person carrying the new baby would climb on to the chair before going downstairs! In some parts of Yorkshire, it was thought that the first person to handle a new baby must be a virgin, a reminder of the birth of Christ from His Virgin Mother.

'Another common belief in some country areas was that a kitten and a new baby could never thrive in the same house, so any kittens were given away or even destroyed. There's maybe some sense in this if the parents were worried about the cats sleeping on the face of a baby and smothering it.

'Good luck charms of the kind mentioned above were put inside the cradle for luck, and one odd surviving idea is that you should never rock an empty cradle. In Scotland, this meant the baby would die but in some parts of England it meant you'd have lots more children! "If you rock the cradle empty,/Then you'll have babies aplenty!"

'In Yorkshire, you never brought a cradle into the house before the birth, and you made sure the cradle was paid for before the baby was placed in it! It was also wrong for anyone to walk between a fire and a cradle containing an unbaptised baby, and if a woman wanted more babies she always kept a cradle in the house.

'In some areas, older women will never allow the bed of a new mother to be turned until the baby is a month old for fear of bringing bad luck, and one of the long-persisting ideas is that during birth, all knots and tied things should be undone and doors opened. Somehow, this was thought to ease the birth.

'Tickling the feet of a newborn baby was understood to make the child stutter in adult life, and if you washed the right hand of the baby before its baptism, it would never enjoy riches.

'Perhaps the strangest idea to survive even today is that the fingernails of a new baby should never be cut until the child is a year old. Mothers would, and still do, bite the nails instead of cutting them. This is a relic of the days when it was thought a baby with cut nails would grow up to be light-fingered, i.e. a thief, and even after that first year had passed there were certain days when cutting fingernails was favoured. "Better a child had ne'er been born than to cut his nails on a Sunday morn." Generally, Monday and Tuesday were very lucky days to perform this task, with Wednesday and Thursday being moderately lucky. Friday and Saturday were poor days from the luck point of view.

'The verse is as follows:

Cut them on Monday, cut them for health;
Cut them on Tuesday, cut them for wealth;
Cut them on Wednesday, cut them for news;
Cut them on Thursday, a new pair of shoes.
Cut them on Friday, cut them for sorrow;
Cut them on Saturday, a present tomorrow;
But he that on Sunday cuts his horn –
Better that he had never been born!'

ON BAPTISM

'Even now, there are mixed ideas about the timing of a baptism. Most Catholics believe it should be done as soon as possible after the birth, while members of the Church of England and other Christian faiths generally have their children baptised after suitable delay, perhaps six or eight weeks, or even longer. The timing is often a personal matter for parents, but the ceremony itself is a fascinating mixture of religion and superstition. Before Christianity, there were elaborate name ceremonies involving purified water and today, in addition to this being the time a person is given a name, it is also a formal acceptance of a child into the Christian faith.

'Not long ago, the trip to the church for baptism was the first outing of a child, the thinking being that an airing while unbaptised was placing the child at risk from illness, troubles of various kinds or even death.

'There was another idea, too, that a child would never thrive until it had been baptised, and so some parents favoured an early ceremony for the general health and benefit of their baby.

'If a boy and a girl had to be baptised together, the boy was always first, otherwise, it was thought he would be without a beard, and less than manly, when he matured. If a girl was baptised first, it was felt she would adopt unwelcome masculine characteristics and grow facial hair.

'There has long been a worry that if a baby sneezes during baptism it heralds bad luck, and it is also a bad omen if the baby refuses to cry when the water is poured over its head. Some thought the cry was the sign of the Devil being forced away from the child and sometimes members of the christening party – parents or godparents perhaps – were told to make the child cry by nipping it!

'One idea in the north of England which persisted until recently was that when the baptismal party was either going to the church or coming from it, they had to present a gift to the first person they met who was of the opposite sex to the baby. This gift was known as the Groaning Cake and used to be a specially made cake, although in recent times it comprised a piece of bread and cheese. It was usually carried by a woman, although not always, and it was thought to ensure good fortune for the baby, albeit something of a surprise to the startled recipient!

'When people go to visit a new baby for the first time, or when a baby is taken for the first time into another house, there is still a tradition that the child be given certain gifts. These vary from region to region, but include an egg, some salt, a piece of white bread or cake, or a piece of silver. Sometimes one item is given, sometimes three, such as the egg, the salt and either the food or silver, the latter two items each representing continuing wealth. The egg symbolises continuing life and the salt ensures purity and an immortal life. In some cases, the salt was placed on the tip of the baby's tongue!'

ON RHYMES

Following these items, Grandad had written a personal note which said, 'When I was a

little lad, my mother used to say all kinds of nursery rhymes when she was caring for me. She would sing some of them and fit them into what she was doing at the time. All the well-known nursery rhymes can be found in other books, and so I will include some Yorkshire variations of one or two, and some which might not be found outside the county.

'One interesting fact is that Humpty Dumpty was written about an event at Cawood Castle which is near Selby in North Yorkshire. This castle was the scene of Cardinal Wolsey's great fall and the legend is that in 1530 he stood on the castle walls to watch "all the king's horses and all the king's men" come to arrest him. He was taken from here to London where he was executed for treason, his crime being that he would not arrange a divorce between King Henry VIII and Catherine of Aragon.

'This nursery rhyme comes from East Yorkshire, where the word "pranked" means "dressed":

Pranketty iddity, pranketty aye
Baby hasn't been pranked today;
But let tomorrow come very soon
And baby'll be pranked long before noon.

'Another Yorkshire one is a variation of "Curly locks, curly locks, wilt thou be mine". In this one, the word "sarrow" means to serve with food. It goes:

Bonny lass, bonny lass
Wilt thou be mine?
Thou shalt not wash dishes
Nor sarrow the swine,
But sit on a cushion
And sew up a seam
And feast upon nothing
But strawberries and cream.

'There's one word of difference in Sheffield in the "Little Miss Muffet" rhyme. Most people sing

Little Miss Muffet sat on a tuffet
Eating her curds and whey
When down came a spider
And sat down beside her
And frightened Miss Muffet away.

'In Sheffield, they used to say buffet which is their word for a stool, whereas in other parts of the country, a tuffet is a low seat.

'We've variations of others too, such as this one:

Diddle, diddle dumpling, my son John
Went to bed with his breeches on;
One stocking off, one stocking on,
Diddle, diddle dumpling, my son John.

'We honour the daffodil with:

Daffy down dilly has come up to town
In a yellow petticoat and a fine gown.

'Now, when the children went to bed in some of the Pennine areas of Yorkshire, they would say:

Matthew, Mark, Luke and John
Bless the bed that I lie on;
Four corners on my bed
Five angels there lie spread
Two near my feet, two near my head
And one at my heart, my soul to keep.

'One verse that was sung in Beckindale, in the playgrounds especially, was a form of the "Pat-a-Cake, Pat-a-Cake Baker's Man" rhyme. It went:

Clap-a-cake, clap-a-cake, Baker's man
Knead and bake it as fast as you can;
Stick it and prick it, and mark it with B
And bake it in t'oven for baby and me.

'The children in Yorkshire would sing playground rhymes too, like this one if somebody was late:

Liggy-bed lollard, ten o'clock schollard
What makes you come so soon?
You used to come at ten o'clock
But now you come at noon.

'A lig-a-bed is someone who lies in bed when it's time to get up; lig means to lie.

'My old mother would often play games with me before I went to bed, such as hiding a sweet in her hand and saying:

Handy-pandy, sugar candy
Which hand are you in?

'I was then supposed to guess and, if I guessed right, I could have the sweet.'

Dolly smiled as she read Grandad's collection of nursery rhymes.

'Aye, I remember one,' Jack said. 'Years ago, my granny used to sing:

Cock-a-doodle doo
My father's gone to plough
My mother's lost her pudding poke
And doesn't know what to do.'

'What's a pudding poke?' laughed Dolly.

'It was a small bag that the women used to cook their puddings in; there was a saying "Never buy a pig in a poke" and that arose because some simple folks would buy a little pig in a bag without opening it to see what condition it was in. One trick was to put a cat inside! When it wriggled about, the seller would tell the buyer it might escape, so he must never open it until he got home – he thought he'd bought a tiny, lively sucking-pig, but in fact had bought a cat! That's where you get the saying about "Letting the cat out of the bag", meaning to reveal a secret.'

'My! You are full of it!' Dolly smiled. 'So what else has Grandad written?'

'There's lots of verses that children sing about the weather and other country matters, but isn't this the place for me to include your various children's games?'

'Right, you read me those other sayings, and I'll get my games ready to follow.'

'Right,' and he began to read a host of smaller verses, including:

'"Friday Flit; short sit" – that means people who move house on a Friday seldom stay long in that house.

'"Never cast a clout till May be out" – they say this means the month of May, but I reckon it means the blossom we call may. That's the blossom of the hawthorn which appears in the middle of May; it's very strong smelling and smothers the hedgerows. It's a beautiful sight – and, I might add,' he grinned at Dolly, 'that's the may in the song "Here we go gathering nuts in May". If you think about it, that verse is nonsense: it goes "Here we go gathering nuts in May, on a cold and frosty morning". The point is that nuts aren't ready for gathering in May, so the verse should really read "knots of may", meaning bunches of may blossom. Then it makes sense because some May mornings can be frosty.'

Jack continued. 'There are weather songs like "Rain, rain go away, come again another day" or "Rain, rain go to Spain; Fair weather come again". There's others like this:

I see the moon, the moon sees me
God bless the sailors on the sea.

I see the moon, the moon sees me,
God help the parson that baptised me!

Snail, snail, shoot out your horn
And say if it'll be fine on the morn.

Spring: Slippy, drippy, nippy!
Summer: Showery, flowery, bowery!
Autumn: Hoppy, croppy, poppy;
Winter: Wheezy, sneezy, breezy.

Onion skin, very thin
Mild weather coming in;
Onion skin, thick and tough
Coming weather cold and rough.

When snow and frost are both together
Sit by the fire and spare shoe leather.

Snow, snow give over
The cows are in the clover.

The moon shines bright,
The stars give light
And little Nancy Buttercup
Will come tomorrow night.

Sticks and stones will break my bones
But calling never hurt me!'

ON GAMES

After this, Jack smiled at Dolly. 'Well?'

'I've a list here,' she showed him a pile of her own notes. 'The snag is that children all seem to make up their own rules, so the games do vary a lot from place to place. There are new games coming all the time – there are lots of clapping games; for example, the other day, I heard some girls chanting as they clapped their hands to: "I'm only a poor little Ewing; JR's always being cross with me; Sue Ellen's a drunk, The baby's a punk, And Bobby lives under the sea." Some clapping games become very complicated, because hands are clapped in a special sequence, sometimes the players smacking the palms of partner's or other players' hands or clapping their own in time to the verses. One is:

Under the bramble bushes
Down by the sea
My love for you, darling,
Your love for me.
When we get married
We'll raise a family
A boy for you, a girl for me
And that's the way it's going to be.

'One popular clapping game was played to the words: "My mother said, that I never should, play with the gypsies in the wood. If I did, she would say, go again another day."

'Some games are variations of very old ones, especially the hide-and-seek games, which are still popular with differing rules under all sorts of names.

'There's wolf-and-sheep, fox-and-chicken, puss-in-the-corner, fox-off and many more. The general rule is that one player has to catch or find the others, sometimes before they reach the safety of "home". For example, in puss-in-the-corner, puss stands in the middle of the room or playground and the mice all hide. When a mouse is in a corner – and there's not enough corners for all – it is safe, so for this game, at a given signal, they must all run from safety and try to reach a corner before puss catches them. When puss catches a mouse he is out, or sometimes that mouse becomes the puss, and the game starts again.

'In the fox-and-chickens, one player is the fox who is hiding and another is the mother hen. All the other players are chickens, and they are assembled around mother hen. The fox comes out of hiding and sees mother hen with her chicks. "What do you want?" asks mother hen. "A chicken for supper," says the fox, and he rushes to seize a chicken. Mother hen spreads her arms as all the chickens hide behind her; each chicken must hold the waist of the one before, the front one holding mother hen's waist. And the fox has to try to get past the hen to touch one of the chickens.

The game continues until there are no chickens left, the fun being in a long line of chickens trying to move together out of the clutches of the fox. There was a similar game called "sheep, sheep come home". A wolf stood in the middle of the playground, with a shepherd at one end. The sheep were at the other end and had to reach the shepherd without being caught.'

'We played fox-off as lads,' Jack remembered. 'We were all foxes, except one who was a huntsman. The foxes hid and the huntsman had to find them. We liked to play this in the woods. When the huntsman found a fox, the fox had to run and if it was caught, that fox became a huntsman and helped in the search; as each fox was found and caught, it became a huntsman and helped to find the others. The last fox to be found was the winner and became the first huntsman for the next game. The trick was to hide so no one knew where you were, and to run as fast as you could when you had been found! That was a smashing game of chasing and hiding!'

'That was a lads' game,' said Dolly. 'Like cock-o'-the-midden. One boy stood on some high place, and the others tried to dislodge him. But the girls played lots of kissing games and loved to get the boys to join in. One popular kissing game involved persuading a boy to stand in the centre of a

moving circle of girls as they sang:

Here the poor widow stands
With all her children on her hands;
One can bake, one can brew
One can make lily white dough;
One can sit by the fire and spin
One can make a bed fit for a king,
And who'll choose one of my
daughters?

'As they moved around him the boy had to make his choice by kissing her, then taking her into the centre of the ring. Now the remaining girls sang:

Now you're married, we wish you joy
First a girl, and then a boy
Another kiss and then a smile!

'They left the ring, and another boy took their place as the game restarted until some unfortunate girl or boy was left with little or no choice! One popular alternative for the final lines was:

Choose to the east, choose to the west,
Choose the one that you love best.
When you're married, she must obey,
You must be true in all you say.
You must be kind, you must be good
And help your wife to chop the wood.'

'Weren't there lots of skipping games, too?' asked Jack.

'Oh, yes, lots,' said Dolly. 'Many of them were played as people chanted nursery rhymes. Two girls would turn a long rope and all the others would take turns and attempt to jump into it and skip for as long as possible. If you tripped over the rope, you were out. The last one to survive was the winner. Sometimes, the two holding the rope would try to snatch a skipper as they sang the last word of this verse:

There was a jolly miller and he lived by
himself;

As the mill went around, he gained his
wealth.
One hand on the hopper, the other in
the bag
And as the mill went round, he made
his grab!'

'I remember a skipping game when I was at school,' Jack said. 'As the skipper skipped, the others sang: "Raspberry, strawberry, gooseberry jam; tell me the name of your young man." If the skipper did not trip during this, it was sung faster next time, getting faster and faster until it was impossible to keep pace. But there are hundreds of games, too many to include here. Look at the different ways of playing marbles, for example, games with hoops which come and go as the mood of fashion changes, a bewildering number of ball games, some with bats and some without, hop-scotch, tiddlywinks, ring-a-ring-a-roses, leap frog (we played with teams; one bent down, each man behind his mate. The other team jumped on one by one and tried to smash us to the ground with their weight!). And, of course, there was tig! Somebody is "on" and he or she chases all the others, trying to touch them; once they're touched or tigged, they're out. The last to be tigged is "on" for the next game.'

'Aye,' smiled Dolly. 'And I've got something different here. An old lady gave me a strange verse that shows some of the games that were being played in the 17th century. I wondered if that might be of interest?'

'It's a bit before our time, but I think it might get folks wondering what some of them were! We'll include it!'

Dolly produced a yellowed piece of notepaper in faded ink which said, 'This is a verse listing some games played by country folk in the 17th century:

'Man, I dare challenge thee to throw the
sledge,

To jump, or leap over ditch or hedge,
To wrestle, play at stoolball or to run
To pitch the bar, or shoot off a gun.
To play at loggets, nine-holes or ten-pins
To try it out at football by the shins.
At tick-tack, Irish, noddie, maw or ruff,
At hot-cockles, leap-frog or blind-man's buff,
To drink half-pots or deal at the whole can,
To play at base, or pen-and-ink horn, sir, I can.
To dance the morris play, the barley-break.
At all exploits a man can think or speak.
At shove-groat, venter-point or cross and pile

At beshrow him that's at yonder stile.
At leaping o'er a midsummer bonfire
Or at drawing Dun out of the Mire.
At shoot-cock, Gregory, stool-ball and what not
Pick-point, top, and scourge to make him hot.'

'Well,' said Jack. 'There's a few games mentioned there that I've never heard of. But I reckon Grandad would want them included for old times' sake! So, thanks Dolly. Now we've a nice collection of a few things about children.'

'A sooart o' skeg ower bairn-laikings?' smiled Dolly.

'Aye,' said Jack. 'That's about it.'

CHAPTER EIGHT

ON BIRDS, BEES AND BUTTERFLIES

When the eagle is dead, the crow
will pick his eyes out.

Sam Pearson's notebook

J ack Sugden and Henry Wilks had met in the parlour of Emmerdale Farm to discuss the financial year end and the arrangements for auditing the books of Emmerdale Farm Ltd. Now that their discussions were over, each was enjoying a tumbler of fine malt whisky and a few moments of relaxation in front of the fire.

'Tell me, Jack,' Henry said. 'This book of your grandfather's. Donald Hinton mentioned it – he said summat about you publishing it?'

'Aye. Grandad left it to me, I'm checking the contents when I've a moment, Henry. I'm not certain whether I'll have it published. Did he talk to you about it?'

'Oh, yes, quite often. About birds mainly, and some other aspects of country lore. He wasn't too interested in modern information, Jack. He said he was recording the past, old-time beliefs, customs, that sort of thing. He didn't want the old-fashioned way of life to vanish without trace and said his notebook would do a little to keep things alive!'

'That's Grandad all over!' laughed Jack. 'Anyway, I'm getting his book checked, making sure he's not duplicated anything for example, or missed bits out. I know he talked to lots of folks, but was still awaiting their help when he died. Hang on, I'll get it, then I can pick your brains while you're here.'

Jack returned with the old notebook and opened it at the section marked *Birds*. He smiled. 'He's got your name here, Henry. It says "Henry Wilks was a great help in providing information for much of this chapter." So there you are, Henry, your name in lights!'

'Ha!' Henry chuckled. 'Fame at last! I was just pleased to help. So what's he written, Jack? You tell me and I'll add bits where I can. Got a pencil handy, have you?'

The page fell open at the item about magpies.

ON MAGPIES

'I'm starting with magpies because there's still a lot of superstition about them. Here in Yorkshire, we call them nanpies, long-tailed nans, pynots or tell-pie-tits! One old verse said: "Tell-pie-tit, Laid an egg and couldn't sit!" At one time, they were very common, then they became scarce in many rural parts because gamekeepers shot them. They can be a menace by killing baby animals and birds or stealing eggs but they're not as harmful a bird as many think. In recent years, their numbers have increased and in some areas there are large flocks of them. They've now become a familiar sight in towns and large cities. They've a tendency to steal shiny trinkets or bits of tinfoil which they carry to their nests. Country folk always said you could teach a magpie to talk but said you had to slit its tongue first.

'They're beautifully coloured; from a distance they look like black and white birds with long tails, but the colours of their back, wings and tail are glossy blue, green, purple and even red, all very dark. When the light reflects from them, they're gorgeous – but very cheeky!'

Henry laughed. 'Aye, they are. I was in Leeds once, in Roundhay Park, when one swooped down and pinched half a sandwich that a man had put down for a moment beside him on a bench! That same day, probably the same magpie flew over a chap walking his dog and the chap stopped, made the sign of the cross and then spat into the grass!'

'Recently?' asked Jack.

'Within the last five years!' vowed Henry. 'There's still a lot of superstition surrounding magpies.'

'Grandad's got it here,' Jack pointed. 'He starts with that famous verse:

One for sorrow, two for joy

Henry Wilks

Three for a girl and four for a boy;
Five is for silver and six is for gold
And seven's a secret never to be told.
Eight's for heaven and nine is for hell
And ten is for Satan his very self!'

Grandad's book went on, 'The lines of this verse alter from place to place. Some say "One for sorrow, two for mirth/Three for a wedding, four for a birth". Another variation is that "Five is for heaven, six is for hell/And seven's for the Devil himself".'

Jack added. 'He's got several verses here. Listen to this: "One's a sign of mischief, two's a sign of mirth, three is a sign of a wedding and four's a sign of birth; five's a sign of rain and six is a bastard bairn!" There's another: "One's a sign of bad luck, two's a sign of good; three's a sign of a broken leg and four's a sign of a wedding." And this one? After the usual first four magpies which he's mentioned in that first verse, there's this: "Five is a parson, six for a clerk, seven for a baby buried in the dark!"'

'The point is this,' added Henry. 'It's always been thought bad luck to see a magpie on its own. It'll bring sorrow of some kind. But you could avoid that bad luck by spitting or making the sign of the cross while bowing towards it, or crossing your fingers! And, Jack, believe it or believe it not, there's folks still think like that! There's an old verse: "I crossed the pynot/And the pynot crossed me;/The Devil take the pynot/And God save me."'

'Grandad's notes say it's always been a bird of evil.' Jack scanned the pages. 'One tale says it refused to dress in full mourning for the death of Christ because it kept its white parts. Another yarn is that it refused to enter the Ark along with the other birds, and that it fluttered around outside, shouting abuse at everybody who drowned!'

He continued, 'To bring good luck, you should see two magpies at the same time – one old notion was that one lot of bad luck cancelled out another, but if you want the good luck, or the other benefits the verse

mentions, you must do more than just see the bird. You've got to spit towards it, remove your hat and say "Devil, Devil, I defy thee!"'

'So that's why my luck never changes even when I see a magpie!' laughed Henry. 'But there is a genuine angle to this sighting of one bird. Fishermen would quote this, and I never mentioned it to Sam Pearson. Take this down, Jack.'

Jack prepared himself with a pencil and paper, as Henry said, 'Fishermen always reckoned that if they saw a single magpie it meant a bad day's fishing. If they saw two, then a good day was assured. Now magpies are equal partners when raising a brood – the cock and the hen both share the work. In bad weather, a solitary magpie will leave the nest in search of food, the other remaining behind to look after the chicks or eggs. In good, fine and warm weather, both birds will venture out. So there's some sense in one magpie meaning sorrow and two meaning joy – especially if you're a fisherman or on holiday, or if you're a country person who needs good weather for work!'

'Grandad's got a note that if three or four are seen flying together, making harsh calls to each other, then wind is forecast.'

'They say the same about jackdaws, Jack – they're both members of the crow family, so their behaviour can be similar. And the behaviour of rooks foretells the weather.'

'And Grandad adds crows and ravens; if one is seen hanging around a house, perching on the roof or fluttering in front of a window, it heralds a death, so they say!'

'Some folks swear that is true, Jack!' Henry sipped his drink. 'You can't scoff at genuine beliefs! If you meet a single crow, that's unlucky; if one perches anywhere in a churchyard, there'll be a funeral there within a week and if all the rooks (also members of the crow family) desert a wood, there'll be a problem there very soon afterwards. I once knew some rooks desert a wood, and within a year, all the elms there were found to have Dutch elm disease!'

'Get away, Henry, they can't know that!'

'Don't you be too sure, Jack. Now, what other birds has Sam included?'

'Swallows, swifts, cuckoos, owls, robins …and more! I'll read on.'

ON SPARROWS

'"You'll never see a sparrow without its marrow!" That means sparrows go around in pairs or greater numbers, and if they chirp a lot at dawn, bad weather is coming. Sparrows are cheeky birds and there's a warning for them: "A sparrow flying behind a hawk thinks that the hawk is fleeing!"'

ON SWALLOWS

'The countryman knows that when the swallows are flying high, there's fine weather to come. This is true because they chase the insects – and it's the insects that are really forecasting the weather, but you can't see them! The saying goes, "When the swallows fly high, 'tis a sign of dry."

'The opposite is the case when swallows fly low and dip into the rivers and ponds. That means rain. Maybe it's best to mention here that most of the lore about swallows also applies to martins – and that means house martins and sand martins. In fact, some folks used to think the swallow and the house martin were the male and female of the same species, an idea summed up in this verse: "The martin and the swallow/Are God Almighty's shirt and collar."

'They arrive in England in the spring, with the swallows and sand martins usually being first and the house martins coming a week or two later. Swifts, which are not related to the swallows or martins, come after them as a rule.

'One piece of lore says that if there are more swifts than swallows, then we can expect a warm and dry summer, but because the martins often come early, it's said that "When the martins appear, winter has broken." As a rule, there's no frost once the martins arrive, but this is summat you can never be sure of in Yorkshire!

'Another thing about swallows is that they are said to be lucky birds; a swallow's nest at a house brings good luck to the household and some country folk even now leave shed doors open to entice swallows inside to build their nests. This idea comes from ancient times when it was said the swallow helped God to create the sky; some continental peoples refer to them as chickens of the Lord, while in parts of England, especially in Lincolnshire, they're known as birds of blessing.

'Before we knew much about bird migration, it was thought that swifts spent the winter sleeping in the mud at the side of ponds, and that swallows grouped themselves together by linking beaks and wings and then hibernating under the sea. This was an attempt to explain the curious disappearance of these birds over the sea, but now we know they are capable of flying thousands of miles to winter in the sunshine. One odd thing in Yorkshire is that we often get a patch of bad weather about the times of arrival and departure of the swallows. We call them swallow storms, but it's a wise saying that one swallow does not make a summer. And I'll bet the "first swallow" seen by lots of folks isn't a swallow at all – it'll be a house martin.

'The swallow is dark blue and white with a red chin and a long forked tail; and the sand martin, which lives by the riverside, is a sandy brown and white. Swifts are all black and spend their time flying about and screaming!'

ON THE CUCKOO

'The cuckoo is probably the best-known of the British birds even though most folks wouldn't recognise one if they saw it. They know it from its voice and once you hear that "cuckoo" sound, you know spring has arrived. It's a large bird, just over a foot in length, and it looks very like a hawk, so much so that little birds will sometimes mob it. It has a grey back and wings, with white underparts which are barred with grey. The wings are pointed at the tips, but the long tail is rounded. It's an awful bird, for the female lays her eggs in the nests of other smaller birds, removing one of the small bird's eggs before she lays her own. She might eat this or cast it out of the nest. The cuckoo egg sometimes matches the colours of those in the host nests. And when the young cuckoo hatches, it throws out of the nest all the unhatched eggs and so kills its stepbrothers and stepsisters. If they hatch first, they'll usually die of starvation because the infant cuckoo grows so fast that the parents have to spend all their time feeding it. As it gets bigger, they might even have to stand on its back to feed it.

'In spite of its behaviour, country folk welcome it because its arrival heralds the end of winter. There is a verse:

The cuckoo is a pretty bird, she singeth as she flies
She bringeth us good tidings and telleth us no lies.

'The older folk still turn their money over in their pockets or handbags when they hear the first cuckoo because they think this will bring good financial fortune. In some places, they make a wish at the same time. If you have no money in your pockets at the time, but some at home or in the bank, this is no good. An empty pocket when first hearing the cuckoo means bad luck, so country folk always carry some cash with them in the spring – just in case!

'It doesn't stay long; there's a well-known verse which goes

In April, come he will
In May, he sings all day
In June, he changes his tune
In July, away he'll fly
In August, away he must.
If he's heard in September
It's a thing to remember

And heard in October
Means you're not sober!

'It's the male bird that makes the cuckoo calls, and the female makes a bubbling sound; some say it's bad luck to hear the cuckoo on or after Midsummer Day and there's a saying in Yorkshire that the first cock of hay frightens the cuckoo away. One strange custom in some rural parts when you heard the first cuckoo was to roll in the grass – this was thought to cure backache!

'They say the cuckoo and the nightingale sing in the same month, but up here in Yorkshire you'll rarely, if ever, hear the nightingale. Those who reckon they've heard it have probably heard a blackbird.'

ON OWLS

'Owls are said to be wise birds, but they're no wiser than others. The Greeks started this belief because Athens used to be full of owls. The Greeks said all the owls had been given to their goddess Minerva, who was also known as Athena, and so the owl became her symbol. If you go to Greece now, you can buy little model owls as good luck charms. Because Athena, or Minerva, was the goddess of wisdom, it follows that the owl is also said to be wise. They had a saying "It's like sending owls to Athens" which was like our old saying about sending coals to Newcastle!

'Some old Greek beliefs have survived to this day – one was that if an owl flew over soldiers in battle it was an omen of victory, and another was that if a child was made to drink an owl's egg broken into a cup, then the child would never become a drunkard! Here in England, it was said that eating the powdered egg of an owl could improve a person's eyesight.

'In Britain, of course, there are half-a-dozen different varieties of owl, but the best for the farmer is the barn owl. It kills vermin and if you look closely at old barns in the

Yorkshire Dales you'll see holes in the walls and doors. These were made so that barn owls could get inside to nest and to hunt rats, mice and other pests. We call them screech owls because of their ghastly screams, and lots of folks were terrified of them at night because they look like a white ghost when flying. They make no sound when flying either, their soft feathers making this possible. Tan on top, and pure white beneath, they are getting rarer, and I do know that farmers in the Dales will be pleased if those people who renovate old barns and other buildings would leave owl windows to encourage these birds to stay.

'The other well-known owl in the woods and countryside is the tawny owl; that's the one that hoots a lot at night. If you hear "too-whit, too-whoo" it's probably two owls calling to each other, one whoo-whooing and the other whitting! In Yorkshire, we call this one the jenny hoolet.

'Country folk would get very upset if an owl of any kind hooted or cried around their house, especially in the daytime; they thought this foretold a death, and they do say that no man should look into an owl's nest, otherwise he will be sad for the rest of his life.

'Other sayings tell us that a screeching owl means stormy weather or that a cold spell is on the way, but when owls hoot at night, then fair weather can be expected. If an owl hoots softly during a storm, it means fair weather is coming soon.

'The other owls in Britain are the little owl, the long-eared owl, the short-eared owl and the very rare snowy owl.'

ON ROBINS AND WRENS

'The robin and the wren
Are God Almighty's cock and hen.
Him that harries their nest
Shall never let his soul have rest.

'There was an old belief that the robin and the wren were male and female of the same species, which explains a little of this verse. Anyone who hurt either a robin or a wren would never be successful in life and this arose because the robin was thought to be the bird that tried to ease the suffering of Christ on the cross by withdrawing a thorn from His head. In so doing, some of Christ's blood stained the breast of the little bird. Another account of this bird's help to the needy was given in the story of The Babes in the Wood, when a robin redbreast gathered leaves to cover the bodies of the dead children. Tales of this kind have made the robin appear to be a lover of people and so it is, especially in Britain. It's a very tame bird and likes to live around houses and in gardens; in 1961, it was nominated Britain's national bird.

'But the robin is not universally welcome. Even today, there are those who believe a robin is an omen of death, especially if it tries to enter a house or taps at a window; I've known country folk tear robins' nests apart in fear that the young birds would come into the house and so bring about a death.

'For the same reason, some people dislike Christmas cards which depict a robin, and if a robin enters a church and sings on the altar, then it's said there will be a funeral in that church within a very short time.

'Robins live here all the year round, and are very keen on preserving their own territories; that's why they sing a lot. It's their way of telling other robins to keep away! But if a robin sings near a house, it's a sign of rain, and if it goes inside, it's a sign of frost or snow. Sometimes, if the weather is bad, particularly during the spring, and a robin sings from a high branch, then it's a sure indication of fair weather to come. If a robin sings loudly very early in the morning, it means rain and there is this old verse:

If the robin sings in the bush

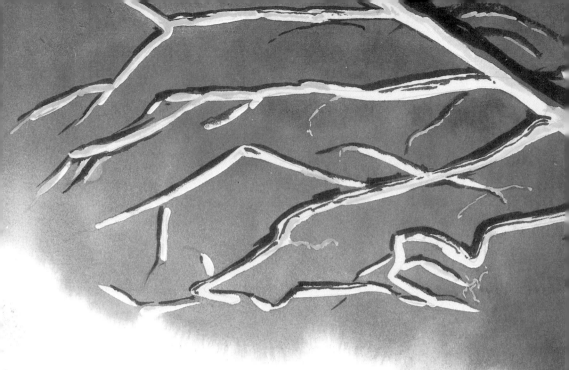

Then the weather will be coarse;
If the robin sings on the barn
Then the weather will be warm.

'Wrens are tiny birds with massive and very musical voices and there used to be a curious custom of hunting wrens on St Stephen's Day, which is also Boxing Day. In some areas, young men would catch and kill a wren, then carry its body around the houses asking for gifts or cakes. If these were not given, it was said that a storm would come and damage the house. This might be linked to a sailors' belief that the dead body of a wren protected ships against storms at sea.

'Another legend behind the hunting of wrens is that the wren lost favour because when St Stephen was about to be executed he managed to escape, but the loud singing of a wren aroused his captors who re-arrested him!

'But it's a lovely little bird who suffers dreadfully during the worst of winters; its tiny size means it cannot withstand the cold and quickly dies. A severe winter can soon reduce the numbers of resident wrens, but its size does enable it to hunt where the larger birds cannot reach. Our love for the wren has given it a nickname of Jenny Wren.'

ON GEESE

'In days gone by, every cottager kept a few geese, chiefly for food. By tradition, the people always ate a goose on Michaelmas Day (September 29th) when geese are at their prime, and an old verse said:

Whosoever eats goose on Michaelmas Day
Shall never lack money, his debts to pay.

'The wing feathers of a goose were used for dusting, the quills of the feathers were for making pens, the fat of a goose was used for making grease which also found value as a cure for colds when rubbed on the chest of a sufferer, and a yard full of geese meant that

SOME YORKSHIRE BIRD NAMES	
Blackbird	Blackie
Blackcap	Coal Hoodie
Blue Tit	Billy Bluecap or Billy Biter
Brambling	French Linney
Chaffinch	Bullspink
Crow	Black Nebbed or Cruke
Cuckoo	Gowk
Dipper	Water Ouzel or Bessy Ducker
Fieldfare	Feltyfare
Goldfinch	Goldspink
Great Black-backed gull	Saddleback
Great Tit	Tom Tit
Greenfinch	Green Linney
Green Plover	Peewit, Tewfit or Teeafit
Green Wood-pecker	Yaffle or Peckatree
Hawfinch	Cherryspink
Hedge Sparrow	Cuddy
Hooded Crow	Hoodie
House Sparrow	Spuggie
Linnet	Red Linney
Long-tailed Tit	Bottle Tit
Missel Thrush	Jeremy Joy or Storm Cock
Nuthatch	Woodcracker
Raven	Corby
Red Grouse	Moor Bird
Redstart	Nanny Redtail
Rook	White Nebbed or Cruke
Skylark	Laverock
Swift	Dicky Devlin
Wagtails (of any kind)	Willy Wagtail
Whitethroat	Nettlemonger
Wood pigeon	Cushat
Wren	Stumpy Tail
Yellow Hammer	Yellow Yowlin or Yellow Linney

nobody could get near the house without the geese making a tremendous noise. They've been used as guards since Roman times, and helped to guard military establishments from saboteurs during the last war. One modern role was to guard a Scottish whisky distillery against intruders!

'But wild geese have provoked a lot of superstition and folklore. Because they make a weird yelping or gabbling sound as they fly overhead in the darkness during migration, the people of bygone times couldn't understand what they were. They couldn't see them and thought they must be the spirits of long-dead people eternally seeking a place of refuge, or the hounds of hell seeking the souls of unbaptised babies. They called them the Gabriel Hounds or Gabriel Ratchets and regarded them as an omen of a death in any household over which they flew at night.

'But both domestic and wild geese make good weather forecasters. When domestic geese become obviously unsettled and bathe themselves a lot, rain is on the way, and if they preen themselves, it usually means wind is coming. If they make a lot of noise or become antagonistic before feeding, it's generally a sign of stormy weather. When wild geese head out to sea in flocks, that sometimes means good weather, but if they remain inland and head for the hills, then storms are due. Wild geese flying high towards the south signifies wintery weather, and some rustics have claimed that a formation of flying geese always forms a figure or a letter which predicts the number of weeks before frost appears!'

ON HENS

Clipped to the pages at this point, Jack found a little note in Grandad's writing which said, 'I mustn't forget the humble farmyard hen!' This was followed by a few notes:

'Hens can forecast the weather just like wild birds. If they huddle together close to the henhouse, especially when they should be going in to roost, then bad weather is coming, and if they play about in the dust and flap their wings, then rain is heralded. "If the hen rolls in the sand, rain is at hand." If hens spend time preening their feathers during a storm, it is about to fair up, and if they stand on one leg, then that suggests it is about to become colder.

When it comes to moulting time, if the cock moults before the hen, we'll have a mixture of fine and cool weather, but if the hen moults first, then it means storms will follow. When a cock crows late or abnormally early, then that means we can expect rain, as we can if all the hens gather on a piece of high ground.

'There are a few old sayings about hens, too, listed here, such as "One chick can keep a hen busy" or "A sitting hen never grows fat."'

ON BIRD GROUPS AND NAMES

Grandad had prepared two lists at the end of this section of his notebook – one was a list of collective nouns for different birds, which appears below; the other, shown opposite, was a list of Yorkshire names for many of the birds seen around the district.

A Gathering of Birds

'A brood of chickens, a covert of coots, a murder of crows, a herd of curlew, a flight of doves, a flight of dunlins, a convocation of eagles, a flock of fieldfares, a charm of goldfinches, a gaggle or skein of geese, a covey of grouse, a covey of partridges, a colony of gulls, an exaltation of larks, a band of jays, a tiding of magpies, a watch of nightingales, a flock of pigeons, a brace of pheasants (two) or a brood when there's a family, a clamour or rooks and a tribe of sparrows.'

ON BEES

'We've had the birds, so how about the bees?' asked Henry as Jack refilled his glass. 'Did Sam include summat about bees and other insects?'

'He used to tell me about the custom of telling the bees,' Jack said. 'And I know he's included a note about that since he was so interested in it.'

'Go on! Does that still happen?'

'In some places, yes. Here, I'll find it for you.'

Jack found the relevant pages and passed them over to Henry while he went out and made a coffee. Henry settled down to the notes, which read:

'Since time began, bees have been regarded as divine messengers and carriers of secrets about the future. Country folk always thought that bees could sense the mood of a household – they didn't like disturbances within the household or anger of any kind, which would upset them. Either they would leave their hive to obtain peace and quiet, or they might even die of sorrow. For these reasons, there was a strong sense of understanding and trust between a family and their bees.

'It was, and still is, the custom to tell the bees of any important event which affects the family – all their successes, failures, courtships, examination results, weddings, births, deaths – in fact, anything of importance.

'It was thought that if the bees were not informed they would leave their hive to find another keeper and so the head of the family, or the one who was bee-keeper among them, would visit the hive and give an account of the event to the bees. He did this simply by talking to them. I know of cases of this within the last ten or fifteen years. If the keeper himself died, however, there was a special ritual. The head of the household, usually the eldest son, or perhaps the widow, had to go to the hives and strike them three times with an iron doorkey from the house. As this happened, he or she had to say "The master is dead." If this was not done, it was thought some further disaster or ill fortune would befall the family; in some areas, the hives were draped with black cloths when the bee-keeper died and when the funeral procession left the house, the hives were turned to face away from the corpse. One odd Yorkshire custom was to give the bees something that had belonged to their deceased keeper – there is on record the story of a widow who ground up her husband's favourite pipe to fine powder and gave it to the bees who, in her words, "Ate it up, every bit!"

'One persistent belief is that the sting of bees is a cure for rheumatism, arthritis and similar ailments. There are many stories of suffering people being cured after being heavily stung by bees, or even by nettles in some cases.

'Don't forget that bees have honey in their mouths but stings in their tails!

'Bees are also useful for forecasting the weather; they'll stay and work near their hives if it is going to be wet or stormy and if it's going to be fine and warm, they will travel a long way to work. There's an old saying that "A bee is never caught in a shower". They also say that if a hard winter is heading our way, bees will build up a large stock of honey.

'The best-known rhyme about bees and the weather is this one:

A swarm of bees in May is worth a load of hay;
A swarm of bees in June is worth a silver spoon;
But a swarm of bees in July, isn't worth a fly.

'Other insects predict the weather in various ways – ants will return to their nests before a storm and will sometimes begin a busy building programme if rain is threatened. Flies come into houses and buildings before a rain storm and if gnats bite a lot, then rain is on the way. Midges dancing high in a column during the evening means fine weather and if there are lots of them about in the spring, then a fine, dry autumn is forecast.

'Spiders aren't insects, strictly speaking, but they seem to anticipate rain or wind by building webs with short strands and if a spider cleans its web, then fine weather is coming. If spiders appear more than usual on the walls of a house, then rain is heading that way and garden spiders seem to anticipate rain by abandoning their webs and creeping away to hide.'

Jack returned with a mug of coffee apiece and Henry expressed his delight with what he'd read. As he sipped his drink, he noticed Grandad's next entry was about ladybirds.

'My favourite insects – along with butter-flies!' smiled Henry.

ON LADYBIRDS

'In some parts of the north of England, children would pick up any ladybird they found and throw it in the air as they chanted:

Reed, reed sodger, fly away
And make the morn a sunny day.

'I've never known ladybirds be called that name in Yorkshire, although one Yorkshire name is cowlady. The Yorkshire version of the ladybird chant is this:

Cowlady, cowlady, fly away home
Your house is on fire, your children have gone
All except poor Nanny sitting under a pan
Weaving gold and lace as fast as she can.

'It's always been thought unlucky to kill a

ladybird, and a sign of good luck if a ladybird settles on your hand or clothes and it should never be brushed away, but allowed to leave at its own desire. Young girls should gently blow it off their hand if they are keen to know the name of their future husband or lover, and then sing this verse: "Fly away east, fly away west/Show me where lives the one I love best."

'Children love to count the spots on a ladybird's back, some thinking that if one settles on your hand, good luck will come for the number of months shown by the spots. The best-known ladybirds have red wings with black spots – some have seven spots, some five and some two. In the winter, dozens of ladybirds will hibernate under window ledges or in cracks around the house and outbuildings, or under tree bark.

'But there are lots of other ladybirds, more than forty different types in Britain. Some are yellow with black spots (one has between sixteen and twenty-four spots, another has twenty-two); there are black ladybirds with yellow or red spots, and a red ladybird with black spots surrounded by yellow lines, making them look like eyes. This has seven or eight spots.

'Any gardener should welcome ladybirds because they kill huge numbers of greenflies and other aphids, one ladybird eating up to fifty aphids per day! They're most useful in a rose garden. A lot of ladybirds in the spring is said to herald a hot, dry summer.'

ON BUTTERFLIES

'In the past, butterflies were associated with the souls of the departed. Many people thought butterflies were the souls of innocent people waiting their turn to enter heaven and for this reason it has always been regarded as wrong to kill any butterfly. In some parts of the Yorkshire Dales, butterflies were once thought to be the souls of unbaptised children who were barred from entering heaven, and therefore committed to a perpetual life on earth. The exception was a red butterfly – this was thought to be a witch and was destroyed on sight.

'One old belief was that if the first butterfly you saw in spring was a white one, then you would enjoy a plentiful supply of white bread that year, white bread then being more costly and highly regarded than brown! This implied that you would have plenty of money.

'So far as the weather is concerned, the early appearance of a butterfly is the sign of a good summer to follow, although when a white butterfly flies in from the south-west, then rain is forecast.

'People would refer to useless characters as butterflies, because they flit from one nice thing to another, but the moment life becomes stormy, they give up! I like the term "butterfly kiss" which means those true, but very gentle kisses or those that are made by the touch of fluttering eyelashes!

CHAPTER NINE

ON BURIALS, BATS AND BELFRIES

*A green winter makes a full
churchyard.*

Sam Pearson's notebook

Mr Wilks tells me you're working on Sam's notebook.' Amos Brearly, landlord of the Woolpack Inn at Beckindale, served Jack with a pint of bitter. 'Now, I happen to know that he did some very serious research, very serious indeed, so that he'd get all his facts accurate.'

'He asked questions all over...' Jack began.

'Aye, and he had to come to a Brearly for the really serious material, tha knaws, he didn't trouble me for any of that flippant stuff, Jack. He appreciated the Brearly intellect in matters of this kind and I do happen to know that he valued my journalistic skills in helping with his material.'

'Grandad recognised a man of infinite wisdom in you, Amos,' smiled Jack. 'I do know he welcomed your contribution.'

'Matters of a grave nature were what he talked to me about, Jack. Important aspects of country life and lore, things of a more enduring nature than ephemeral matters, in a manner of speaking.'

'Like funerals?' grinned Jack.

'Aye, funerals was one thing, matters appertaining to deaths...'

Amos did not notice the gleam in Jack's eyes at Amos's disregard of the little joke associating grave matters with funerals, but pressed on.

'Bidding to funerals, for example,' Amos assumed a superior expression as he gazed into the beams of the Woolpack. 'That's getting folks there in a seemly manner, with compassion for the dear departed and a sympathetic understanding of a family's grief. Now my relations, with their unrivalled experience in organising interments through my Uncle Ezra's funeral parlour, used to bid folks to funerals with the utmost tact and clemency. A very solemn affair, it was. Very delicately undertaken, in a manner of speaking, were our commissions. All

experts in our chosen trade, Jack, and renowned for our forbearance. That's us Brearlys. It follows that your grandfather, in preparing a literary work of this magnitude, would seek expert Brearly guidance and advice.'

'All right, Amos, so what exactly is "bidding"?'

'If you weren't a relative of the deceased you had to be invited to attend the funeral, and that was an honour, Jack. You didn't just turn up, because this was an event, like a wedding is an event, and folks were particular about who came to see off the dear departed. So someone had to issue the invitations. It might be the sexton, the clerk of the parish council, the undertaker himself or a member of the family. In days gone by, the parish dog-whipper might do it – his usual job was to drive dogs out of church during services but he'd take on this solemn office if asked. They had dog-whippers in some parts of Yorkshire until 1862!'

'Really?' smiled Jack.

'Aye, and a very important job it was. Now, bidding. Before a funeral, the bidder dressed in black and went from house to house saying summat like "You are respectfully bidden to the funeral of Mr So-and-So, starting from his home at 1.45pm on Thursday, 1st September, and following at the parish church at 2pm." Once you'd been bidden, you daren't ignore the funeral, Jack. It was an invitation not to be treated lightly. Now, the one thing most folks feared was a pauper's funeral, and so it became customary for all the mourners to pay summat towards the cost of a funeral, and that included those who were bidden. Some would contribute food for the funeral tea and a ham tea was reckoned to be the best. I recall one woman saying she'd buried three husbands, and all with ham!'

'A fine achievement,' Jack commented. 'And they all wore black, didn't they?'

Amos Brearly

'Oh, aye, some wore black for months afterwards. My Uncle Ezra and those in his particular profession allus kept a stock of black clothes – hats, gloves, scarves, top hats and even jackets and overcoats which they lent or hired to folks who were without, although most families kept their own funeral clothes which they handed down from generation to generation for funerals and anniversaries. They'd even hire a black horse from a farmer and it would draw the hearse, or even a suitable cart with the coffin aboard, through the village to the church-yard. Some villages kept a full set of black harness for funerals, including white plumes for the horse's head.'

'A solemn affair,' commented Jack.

'Very solemn and very touching, if you don't mind me saying so,' continued Amos. 'I can remember some funerals where the men wore white silk scarves tied around their silk top hats; they called 'em weepers, probably to lend to folks who couldn't control their emotions. Now, as a mark of

respect, the whole village closed down as the procession passed by. Shops, businesses, houses – they all closed their doors and curtains and the streets would be lined with people who'd not been bidden. They paid their last respects that way, with the menfolk raising their caps or saluting as the coffin passed by. The service in church would be a long affair, with words of appreciation from the vicar and suitable hymns, and after the interment all those bidden would go back to the house of the deceased, or of the next-of-kin. There'd be the traditional ham tea, and a welcome for those who'd come from distant parts. As Yorkshire folks would say, they liked to see the deceased sided-by in a proper and respectful way.'

'Were there any superstitions about a funeral?' asked Jack.

'Oh, aye,' said Amos. 'Nobody wanted to be the first to be buried in a new graveyard nor, for that matter, the last in an old graveyard. I've known folks bury dogs in new graveyards so the first human wouldn't be the first burial there.'

'Why was that?' asked Jack.

'If someone was the first to be buried,' said Amos, 'it was thought their soul would be taken by the Devil, or that it would become the Churchyard Watcher. The soul would never be allowed to leave that churchyard until someone else was buried there, and then that person became the Watcher. The Watcher's job was to find someone else to be buried there and so that ghostly presence would tour the village at night in a ghostly cart, seeking someone to follow them . . . and so that next corpse became the Watcher. If somebody was the last in a full churchyard, that person also became the Watcher. Now, if no more burials could occur there, it was thought that person was destined to be the Watcher for eternity, so churchyards were never closed. They were used over and over again, the very old graves being re-used. Ask any grave digger about that!'

Jack smiled. 'It's odd how these ideas linger in our folk memory.' He sipped his drink. 'I remember somebody telling me that it's a good omen if it rains during a funeral – good for the soul of the departed person, that is – but that if sunshine strikes the face of a mourner during a funeral then that person will be the next to die.'

'Oh, aye, there's a good deal of lore surrounding funerals, Jack. Like it being unlucky to get ahead of the coffin on its way to the grave, or having an odd number of people at the graveside.'

'Unlucky for who, Amos?'

'Sometimes the soul of the departed, sometimes one of the mourners who might be next for the grave.'

'There's one superstition that circulates even now, Amos, especially in villages, and it's the notion that deaths always come in threes.'

'They do, mark my words, Jack. If you go a long time without a funeral, and one then occurs, you'll have another two very soon afterwards. There's another link with the figure three an' all. In Yorkshire, they say it's unlucky for unmarried people to attend three funerals in a row – they should make sure they attend a wedding before going to another funeral, otherwise they'll die un-wed. And,' Amos continued, 'it's unlucky to postpone a funeral for any reason because it means there'll be more deaths in the family very soon. And for the same reason, you should never allow a body to lie unburied over a Sunday. It's unlucky for a bride or anybody who is starting a journey to meet a funeral procession; anyone who has this experience should join the procession and walk with it for a short distance to remove the bad influences.'

EPITAPHS

'That's enough about death, Amos,' said Jack. 'So what other things did Grandad ask about?'

'Well, in a lighter manner of speaking, Jack, we did talk about some of the daft epitaphs that have been written: this one is from a churchyard on the edge of the Moors:

Remember me as you pass by
When I was alive, I was always dry.

'That's in direct contrast to the Hudders-field lady who made her husband's tomb-stone in the shape of a beer barrel. She said he'd been under the influence of drink all his life, so he could remain under it during death! Mind, some fellers hit back at nagging wives on their tombstones:

Here snug in her grave my wife doth lie
Now she's at rest, so am I.
'Another says:

This spot is the sweetest I've seen in my life
It raises my flowers and covers my wife.

'One in Cumbria says:

Tread softly – if she wakes, she'll talk.

'Maybe the worst (about a dead man): is

Beneath this sod lies another.

'One at Skipton, in the Yorkshire Dales, went:

As you are now, so once was I;
As I am now, some day you'll be
So prepare you now to follow me.

'And some wit had added: "To follow I am not content, I do not know which way you went."

'Not far from York, one says:

For all my pains and trouble since birth
All I've gained is this length of earth.

'And if you go to Whitby, Jack, you might find these in the churchyard there:

Sudden and unexpected was the end
Of our esteemed and beloved friend;
He gave his friends an awful shock
By falling into Sunderland dock.

'And this touching one:

Here lie the bodies of Francis Huntrodds and Mary his wife, who were both born on the same day of the week, month and year, Septembre ye 19th, 1600. Marry'd on the day of their birth and after having had 12 children born to them, died aged 80 years, on the same day of the year they were born, Septembre ye 19th, 1680, the one above not more than five hours of ye other.'

'I wonder what they'll write about you, Amos?' smiled Jack.

'It's summat as I'll have to give a bit of thought to,' said Amos. 'Mebbe summat on t'lines of "He was a Brearly" – I mean to say, Jack, you can't say owt better than that!'

'I can, Amos. How's this: how about another pint?'

LYCH GATES AND LYKEWAKES

'Now, let me see, what else did Sam mention that might be within the Brearly knowledge of such things?' mused Amos.

'What about lych gates, Amos?' Jack put to him.

'Oh, aye, now there's a thing. Lych gates. And the lykewake. Now lych gates are the gates you find with arches that span the footpaths at the entrances to most churches. The word lych means corpse, tha knows. The lych gate marks the boundary between consecrated and non-consecrated ground. In days gone by, and in some modern cases, the coffin would rest under this arch before it was carried into church and while it awaited the arrival of the officiating priest. Today, if you look at those lych gates, you'll mebbe find a stone slab in the middle, or a lych cross in wood or stone, and stone slabs at either side. Those slabs, generally the ones in the middle, are lych stones where coffins would rest, and happen them at the side would be seats for the bearers; they'd wait there until the time came to enter the church. Now, you had to be careful about using lych gates. Some would never allow a wedding procession to use the lych gate, for example, for fear it would bring bad luck to the couple, but funerals always had to use them. Weddings would use another entrance, but some lych gates have two ways through, one for funerals and one for weddings and other occasions.

'Nowadays, I've seen weddings use lych gates as settings for photographs, so it seems the old superstitions have died out.'

'You mentioned the word lykewake, Amos. Is that anything to do with that famous walk across the North York Moors? The Lyke Wake Walk, as they call it?'

'Aye, Jack, it is. I'm pleased you asked me about that. Now the Lyke Wake Walk crosses the North York Moors at their highest and widest point, from Osmotherley to Ravenscar. Folks come from far and wide to tackle it. It's a forty-mile hike and it has to be done within twenty-four hours. Those who make the crossing are entitled to wear a little coffin badge! Now, a lykewake was the period of watch over a dead person. When a person died, a member of the family and a stranger had to watch the body until the funeral, and that was usually within twenty-four hours. It was called a wake. All-night vigils in church were called wakes an' all, and so the watch over a body became known as a lykewake, the watch over a corpse. Fascinating, eh, Jack?'

Amos was in full flow now. 'So far as I can tell, Jack, there's no evidence that any of the route of the Lyke Wake Walk was ever used as a funeral processional track, although it might well have been. There's stone age barrows and other burial mounds in that area, but the primitive folks who lived in what are now the Cleveland Hills used to believe that the soul of a dead person flew over Whinney Moor.'

'I once hiked over there!' said Jack. 'Mind, I never saw any corpses or souls!'

Amos never heeded Jack's attempt at humour. 'Now, you're a literary gent, Jack

Sugden, rather like me if I may be so bold, and so you might have come across Sir Walter Scott's version of the Lyke Wake Dirge.'

Jack smiled, 'You mean:

This ae neet, this ae neet,
Every neet an' all
Fire and sleet, and candleleet
And Christ receive thy soul.'

'Aye.' Amos looked a little crestfallen at Jack's knowledge, but continued, 'Well, the original version of that comes from the Cleveland Lyke Wake Dirge, when the Cleveland Hills were all part of the North Riding of Yorkshire. Now, part's in North Yorkshire and part's in the new Cleveland County. Anyroad, the Dirge is reckoned to be the oldest verse in Yorkshire dialect; it was sung around 1616 at funerals in that part of Yorkshire. It's said that the other versions, including Sir Walter Scott's, are likely to be copies of it. It goes like this:

This yah neet, this yah neet
Ivvery neet an' all
Fire and fleet, an' cannle leet
And Christ tak up thy saul.
When thoo frae hence away art passed
Ivvery neet an' all

Ti Whinney Moor thoo cums at last
An' Christ take up thy saul.'

'All good stuff, Amos,' said Jack.
'There's another eight verses...'

'If I find room in Grandad's notebook I
might include them, Amos, but you've
enlightened me about lykewakes and lych
gates. I can tell you're a learned man.'

Amos beamed and, for a moment, Jack
thought he was going to buy him a drink, but
it was not to be.

'Well, Amos, I'd best be off,' Jack said.
'See you.'

'If you need more help with that book...'
began Amos.

'How about sanctuary, Amos? Suppose
somebody sought sanctuary in Beckindale
church?'

'Aye, well, now there's a thing, Jack...'

But Jack had already reached the door of
the Woolpack, and said, 'Another time,
Amos. Another time.'

SANCTUARY

Back at Emmerdale Farm, Jack decided to
see if his grandfather's notebook included
the lore on sanctuary. He was pleased to
find a short reference:

'Some folks still think a wanted criminal
can obtain sanctuary in a church, and this
happened as recently as 1974 when a man
who was wanted for non-payment of a fine
sought sanctuary in York Minster. This is in
spite of the fact that the remaining laws
which allowed sanctuary were abolished in
1697, and others had been scrapped in 1534.

'The sanctuary laws had lasted for over a
thousand years and there is still a stone frith
stool in Beverley Minster, East Yorkshire,
where a fleeing criminal had to sit when he
asked for sanctuary, and Durham Cathedral
has a replica of its sanctuary knocker which
criminals had to use when asking for this
kind of help.

'The idea of sanctuary was that God and
the church could intervene between a
person and the law. If a man genuinely asked
God for forgiveness, he should not be
expected to suffer the ultimate earthly
penalty for his crime. In England, the laws of
sanctuary applied to all felonies (i.e. serious
crimes) and treasons, except high treason.
This meant that someone who had committed one of those crimes was able to enter a
church and ask for sanctuary from the law.

'Upon reaching the place of sanctuary,
the criminal had first to confess to the crime,
and then swear to be faithful to the local
spiritual authorities, as well as the bailiff, the
governors, burgesses and commoners of
the town. He had to wear a badge and swear
he would "beare no poynted wepen, dagger
or knyfe, ne none other wepen against the
king's peace".

'He must also swear to assist in quelling
strife and extinguishing fire and that he
would be ready for this action upon being
warned by the bellman. He had also to "do
his dewte in syngyng and offer at the Masse".
Having done all this, and having agreed to be
banished from the realm after 40 days, the
criminal, or felon as he was known, was
allowed to remain in the church for that 40
days or, in some cases, 30 days. As most, if
not all of the crimes in question carried the
death penalty, this was a wonderful way of
saving one's own life, and it is not surprising
that lots of these felons crept away from the
church to attempt a life of freedom. But those
who remained for the 30 or 40 days, were
fed, protected and entertained by the
parishioners.

'At the end of this period, the felon was
taken before the coroner where he con-
fessed his crimes once more, and then took
a solemn oath to abjure the realm. This
meant he swore to leave the realm for ever
and his thumb was branded with the letter A
to signify this. The coroner then named the

port to which the felon must make his way as soon as possible, travelling bare-foot, bare-headed and carrying a cross. Any deviation from the route made him liable to execution by the ordinary people and he had to take the first available ship from our shores.

'But many never left England. They hid in the forests where they became outlaws; this meant they officially ceased to exist and all their property was forfeited to the Crown!'

ON CHURCHES AND THE DEVIL

Following this short essay, Jack discovered that Grandad had included some further information about churches.

'In Yorkshire, there are many stories about the Devil's interference during the building of churches. The stories usually tell how a village community decided to build a new church, and when the stones were brought to the site, they were removed overnight by some mysterious force and placed on another site. The villagers returned them, but the following night they were moved again. Here, the stories vary; some say that this was the Devil at work, trying to prevent the building of that church.

'Other stories say that the mysterious force was God trying to tell the builders to use another site. These stories are usually linked to churches built in very isolated locations, such as the one at North Ottering-ton, near Northallerton. In some cases, the Devil won the battle – at Gravely in Hertford-shire, for example, it is said he knocked down the church steeple but when he tried to demolish the church at Rudston in East Yorkshire, by throwing a huge stone javelin at it, it was deflected by a mysterious force and landed in earth nearby. It can still be seen there, where it is one of the biggest standing stones in England. It is bigger than the famous Devil's Arrows at Borough-bridge, just off the A1, and is sometimes called the Cleopatra's Needle of the Wolds.

ST MICHAEL'S CHURCHES.

'One thing I've noticed,' Grandad had written, is that most of the churches which are dedicated to St Michael are situated on the top of a hill. St Michael is in fact the Archangel Michael, leader of the heavenly host, and so he was honoured more than the others. The people therefore tried to honour him by giving his churches more prominence, and so they built them on hill tops. There used to be a lot of St Michael churches in the West Country, but many have fallen into ruin, and a famous one is on Skellig Michael, off the Irish coast. This is an island rock and perched upon it, 700 feet above the sea, is a tiny chapel dedicated to St Michael.

Another tale relates to Wykeham in North Yorkshire where the tower is built away from the church. One legend said the Devil moved it away, another says two sisters quarrelled, one building the church and the other the tower on sites of their own choosing, but the truth is the tower belonged to an earlier chapel and it now forms a most unusual lych gate.

'Some folks are still unhappy about being buried at the north side of the church because they say it belongs to the Devil and in some cases, this was left as unhallowed ground, for use in burying suicides or unbaptised babies. In some very old churches, you can still see a small door in the north wall; this is called the Devil's door and was opened during baptisms to let out the evil spirits chased off by the holy sacrament.

'Also around England, there are several Devil's Bridges, Devil's Leaps, Devil's Holes and Devil's Rocks, often named this way

because their presence in a particular place was inexplicable to the simple minds of the time.'

As he read Grandad's notes, Jack learned that Amos.had helped with the contents of this chapter, adding some facts about a range of creatures linked through folklore to death and sorrow.

ON BATS

'One lingering piece of folklore is that bats live in church belfries, and another enduring legend is that bats will try to nest in a woman's hair and become dreadfully tangled up while doing so. The truth is that bats live in all sorts of places – different species preferring differing habitats – and some do make use of old buildings such as castles and abbeys, old mansions, cellars, barns and, of course, churches. Others prefer the outdoors, sleeping in hollow trees, cracks in cliffs, old mine shafts and any other place that offers shelter. There are over a dozen different kinds of bat in Britain, some very rare like Bechstein's Bat or the Mouse-Eared Bat, and others fairly common such as the Pipistrelle and the Long-Eared Bat. And the tale about them nesting in a woman's hair has never been shown to have any substance. It's just another of those long-reigning myths have survived.

'Bats are protected by law; they're harmless and most useful to the countryside, for they eat literally tons of the insects which are so harmful to our crops. One tiny bat can consume up to 3,500 flies each night, but because they fly at night and have such peculiar wings of dark skin they have become the object of fear and suspicion. This is so unnecessary. They are delightful creatures and so useful, a true friend of any farmer. When bats fly at night to chase insects they issue little squeaking noises, but they navigate by making very highly pitched sounds which a human cannot hear. The bat listens to their echo; it can interpret this to determine the presence of a moth or fly, or an obstacle of some kind, and it is so highly developed that it can catch flies or moths in flight by this system. Bats are not completely blind but have very poor eyesight, so this system of communication is vital to their survival.

'In common with birds which prey on insects, bats are useful forecasters of our weather. If they fly late in the evening, or become very boisterous and numerous in flight, then a fair day will follow, but if they make a lot of noise, or try to fly into buildings, then rain is due. When they saw a bat, some children in East Yorkshire would chant:

Black bat, bear away
Come down by here-away
And come again another day
Black bat, bear away.

'This was done to avert any bad luck that might be brought by the bat, and it was thought that if a bat flew three times around a house, then someone in that house would shortly die. One curious belief in the Isle of Man was that if a bat fell upon you, then it was a sign of impending good fortune, although this seems to contradict the old notion about a bat getting tangled in a woman's hair!

'For folks that do get bats in their belfry, or in any other building including their private house, it must be remembered they are strongly protected by law and that expert advice should be sought if they have become a nuisance. One trick was to position a stuffed barn owl in the building, the idea being that this would frighten away the bats, but even that device could now contravene the existing law.'

ON TOADS AND FROGS

'It used to be thought that if you killed a toad then rain would fall, and the general idea was that it is lucky to meet a toad when you are travelling. If you see a toad hurrying towards water, or lots of them congregating in the evening, then rain will soon fall.

'In the spring, toads will leave their places of hibernation to trek in huge numbers to ponds for spawning. Hundreds will get killed while crossing roads or lanes, and some local authorities are now constructing toad tunnels to allow a safe passage, or erecting road signs to warn motorists that toads can be expected to be crossing a particular road.

'Toads have dry, lumpy skins and, when frightened, can exude a smelly fluid which does not make them attractive to people, but because they kill so many pests they are most useful to gardeners and can become quite tame. They have a curious, slow walk and do not hop like frogs, and criminals once thought if they carried a dead toad in their pockets, they would avoid being detected while committing their crimes.

'One long-standing belief is that toads can live for centuries while incarcerated in rock without any air, food or water. Within recent times, stories have circulated about quarrymen breaking open solid rocks to find a live toad inside, in all cases the men denying that there was any entrance to this place of rest. I reckon that's just a country-man's tale!

'Another surviving legend concerns the fabulous toad-stone. This was said to be a jewel which came only from the heads of aged toads who were on the point of death. These were small, smooth stones of dark grey or light brown and were considered ideal for bringing luck. They were worn as jewellery, sometimes as part of a ring, and it was thought they were capable of changing colour if witches were trying to bewitch the wearer, or if any drink held by the wearer had been poisoned. The stones were difficult to identify, sometimes being described as toad-shaped, but one method was to show one to a toad. If it was true toad-stone, the toad would leap towards it and try to seize it!

'In *As You Like It*, Shakespeare said that the toad, ugly and venomous, wore a precious jewel in its head and in 1589, Thomas Nashe (1567–1601) wrote "It fareth with finer wits as it doth with pearl". The term toad-stone is still applied to some precious stones which have the shape of toads.

'Frogs are far more lively and can be found in most damp areas; a frog is more colourful than the toad, its colouring often blending with its surroundings, and it is also a fine friend for the gardener. It consumes pests like slugs and snails and, like the toad, it is a good weather forecaster. One con-tinuing idea is that frogs are sometimes rained from the skies, but the skin of a live frog really can predict the weather. If the skin is more green than brown or yellow then rain can be expected, and if the skin is dull to the touch, that also means rain. A frog skin with a healthy feel to it is an indication of fine weather, while a frog whose skin is more of a yellow colour is a sign of a good haytime and

therefore of fine weather. When frogs make a lot of noise, it heralds rain; the louder their noise, the more rain there will be.

'It used to be thought that if a frog entered a house it was a sign of death, but some would hang a live frog in their chimneys as a cure for whooping cough!

'One peculiar object obtained from frogs was the magic bone. Possession of one gave a man power over horses, but love-sick girls believed it helped them find a lover.

'To obtain this bone, you had to kill a frog and bury it in an ant-hill for a month, taking it up at new moon. It was now a skeleton, and this was thrown at midnight into a swiftly-flowing stream. It was believed that the magic frog bone would detach itself and float to the surface. The girl then had to secretly fasten this bone to the clothing of the man she desired while saying:

I did not want to hurt this frog
But my true lover's heart to turn;
Wishing that he no rest may find
Till he come to me and speak his mind.

'It was thought the man would then seek out the girl and declare his love for her.'

SNAKES

Grandad had written a short note to say, 'Because the adder is the only poisonous wild snake in Britain, and because there are lots of them on our moors, I felt I'd better include some notes about it.

'The first thing is that there are two other snakes, and one lizard that everybody thinks is a snake. The snakes are:

Adder

'(Also known as viper.) Most common of the three; poisonous and identified by a black zig-zag pattern along the spine. The background can be grey or brown, with variations of these colours; the male can grow up to 2 ft in length, the female a little longer.

Smooth Snake

'Very rare, found only in the south. Colour varies from grey to reddish-brown. Can reach 2 ft in length. Harmless to humans.

Grass Snake

'Fairly common in the lowlands. Olive green or grey green colour, varying from dark to light. The female can grow up to 4 ft in length, the male to about 3 ft. Several may lay their eggs in one manure heap where the heat of decaying matter will hatch them; lots of grass snakes can result! They are harmless to humans.

Slow Worm

'This is not a snake, but it looks just like one. It is a lizard without any legs and its smooth colour can vary from grey to brown. An asset to any garden, it eats slugs and other pests, and is totally harmless to humans.

'The general folklore applies to all snakes, such as:

The first thunder of the year
Wakes all the frogs and all the snakes.

'It is said that when snakes are seeking food rain is to be expected, and this also applies when there is a lot of activity among snakes. They do tend to emerge from their hiding places just before rain, and this makes them vulnerable to those who wish to kill them.

'But it is the adder which has attracted individual attention and our forefathers were frightened of them; they were creatures of ill omen. One on the doorstep signified a death in the household and if you managed to kill the first adder you saw in the spring, you would conquer all enemies!

'Adders like to bask in the sun and are very shy if you leave them alone, but the worried folks of the past always tried to kill the adder.

This could be done only with an ash stick; you had to draw a circle on the ground around the adder, put a sign of the cross inside the circle and quote the first two verses of Psalm 68. This immobilised the adder, but you could not kill it until sunset. When it was eventually killed by hitting it with an ash stick, the skin was taken indoors and hung inside the chimney to ensure good fortune. Some believed the skin of an adder, when applied to the head, cured headache and that when wrapped around the affected part, it would cure pains like rheumatism.

'If an adder bites anyone (which is a very rare occurrence if you leave them alone), you should keep the patient calm and seek medical help. These bites are very rarely fatal in humans, but when they occur it is often in remote country areas. You could tie a restrictive bandage at the heart side of the wound to prevent circulation of the poison, loosening the bandage every half hour for about half a minute, until a doctor or hospital is found.

'In Yorkshire, we call adders hagworms. There is a continuing belief that the female will swallow her young when alarmed but this is not true – they take shelter beneath her belly, reappearing only when danger has passed.'

CHAPTER TEN

ON MARRIAGE, MARKETS AND MOUNTAINS

There is never a Saturday without some sunshine.

Sam Pearson's notebook

K athy Bates, now Mrs Jackie Merrick, had arranged a small dinner party for her new husband and their guests; they were her mother, Mrs Caroline Bates, Annie Sugden and Jack Sugden and it was Kathy's way of thanking them all for their support and help during the first months of her married life. Annie had given the bright and happy young woman the freedom of the Emmerdale kitchen, and she had produced a delightful meal.

Afterwards, Kathy and Jackie said they would wash up and clear the table, allowing Annie, Jack and Caroline Bates to relax with their drinks in the parlour. Inevitably, the talk turned to the wedding and Jack took the opportunity to bring up the subject of Grandad's book.

'You know, Ma, when Kathy's wedding dress got ruined by that burst waterpipe and you came to her rescue with your own wedding dress, you were reviving a bit of folklore about weddings.'

'I know, Jack. You mean the saying about "Something old, something new, Something borrowed, something blue".'

'Aye, you helped to secure their good fortune by doing that!'

Caroline Bates smiled. 'I'd already seen to that, Jack,' she chided him. 'I'm a firm believer in tradition, and I told Kathy about that verse.'

'I guessed you would!' Annie liked to follow the traditions of old, especially for such an important matter as a wedding.

'Kathy insisted on having something old, so she had a tiny lace handkerchief which had belonged to my grandmother,' Caroline told them. 'Then she had something new – all her underclothes, for example, and something borrowed. She had your wedding dress, Annie, but also the veil; she borrowed that from an old family friend. And she had something blue – but that wasn't for your eyes, Jack!'

'So what about the other rules on colour, Caroline?' Jack asked. 'Did you check on those before the wedding?'

'We did. The luckiest colours for the wedding dress are white, silver, various shades of blue or even greys, fawns and tan colours. Gold is suitable and so is pink. But to bring the best of luck, something blue must always be worn; years ago, this was often in the form of little ribbons which were loosely fastened to the wedding dress. Afterwards, the lads picked these off and kept them as good luck charms! We found out that black must never be worn by a bride because it suggests a death very soon, and purple is a sign of mourning too. Green – the fairies' colour – should never be worn either; some would never allow green in the decorations of the room where the reception was held, and in some extreme cases, not even green vegetables were eaten at the wedding breakfast!'

Jack added, 'Grandad had a note which said that to marry in brown means you'll never live in a town, but that was a hint that you'd never be rich enough to do that, so brown's not a very good colour. And red is very unlucky – it symbolises blood!'

'But colours are all right for the bridesmaids,' added Caroline Bates. 'But not greens or blacks or any of those unlucky colours. I learned something about the veil too. Years ago, it was believed that the Devil and his evil spirits would try to take away a woman whose beauty created desire in him, and so a lovely young bride was always advised to hide her face as she walked to her wedding ceremony. Once she was in the church under the protection of God, and safely within reach of her husband-to-be, she could then lift her veil to reveal her prettiness.'

'One thing interested me about our Jackie,' Jack commented. 'Even when Kathy was undergoing all those worries about her

Kathy Bates

dress, Jackie wouldn't go near her. Even a young lad of his generation, in the latter part of the twentieth century, believes it is unlucky for a groom to see the bride in her dress before the wedding ceremony.'

'It's also unlucky for the bride to see herself in a mirror fully dressed in her gown before the ceremony,' Annie added. 'What most brides do is to leave something off as they check their appearance – a shoe, say, or their gloves.'

'Grandad's notes say that in some villages, the bride and groom would walk to church,' Jack told them. 'They went separately, the bride going first accompanied by the best man, and the groom following with the bridesmaids. The parents of the couple weren't part of this procession and there was an old notion that the presence of the bride's mother meant bad luck! I'd better say no more about that! In those days, it didn't matter if the groom saw the bride before the wedding ceremony – this seems to be a comparatively new idea. The original pur-

pose of the best man and the bridesmaids was to protect the bride from anyone who might attack the wedding party and carry off the bride! It seems this used to be a common occurrence. Now there's a superstition that it is unlucky for a girl to be bridesmaid more than three times. This means she will never marry – unless she keeps going until she's been bridesmaid seven times.'

'One thing I had to be careful about,' continued Caroline Bates, 'was that Kathy got safely to the church. I know it's a bride's privilege to be late, but for good luck to continue the bride must leave her home by the front door, leading with her right foot over the threshold, and she must avoid meeting officials like doctors, lawyers, policemen or even blind people. They mean bad luck in the shape of some kind of trouble involving those persons, and it's unlucky to meet a funeral or even a pig! But it is lucky to meet a black cat or a chimney sweep carrying his brushes and covered in soot.'

'And,' beamed Annie, 'the sun must shine

on the bride during her journey to church. Happy is the bride the sun shines on, as they say. It didn't shine on Kathy, but she had plenty of luck in other ways, so I'm sure she'll have a long and happy married life. It's also lucky if she sees a rainbow on her way to church – or an elephant! There's not many elephants in Beckindale!'

At that point, Jackie and Kathy returned to the room and offered to refill the glasses. All accepted, and invited the couple to join them.

'Only for a short while, then,' smiled Jackie. 'I want an early night, we've an early start tomorrow.'

'You'll tell us anything!' laughed Jack. 'Anyroad, now you're both here, did he carry you over the threshold, Kathy?'

'Yeh, 'course he did,' she blushed.

'Why, shouldn't I have done?' blustered Jackie.

''Course you should,' Jack said. 'But why did you do it?'

'Why? Well, because that's what I'm supposed to do, isn't it?' Jackie looked at them all, wondering if this was a leg-pull.

'We all do it,' Jack said. 'I just wondered if you knew why. You young folks usually question everything we old 'uns used to do, so I wondered if that extends to wedding customs.'

'It's to bring luck, isn't it?' Caroline said.

'No, it's just an old custom,' Jack said. 'Years ago, a man would grab a woman and carry her to his home without any formal ceremony. She would kick and scream to get away, but if he got her over the threshold, he'd won. So there you are. In some parts of Yorkshire, there'd be a little reception party at the bride's new home, waiting for her to be carried over the threshold. As this was done, a plateful of shortbread crumbs was thrown over her, but it had to fall on the ground outside. I think that was some kind of fertility symbol. Like confetti.'

'Confetti? A fertility symbol! Don't be daft!' laughed Jackie.

'It's right,' said Caroline. 'Rice used to be thrown over a bride and groom when they left the church, a reminder of the time when rice indicated fertility. In some countries, they threw nuts for the same reason, or gave nuts as presents to newlyweds. And a good nutting year meant lots of boy children. Now, we throw confetti instead – it's a custom going back to pagan times and its original purpose was to encourage childbearing and fertility. In some places, slippers were thrown after the bride for the same reason, so that's why some folks tie old shoes on the back of the going-away car.'

'If you really look at what we twentieth-century people do at weddings, you'd be amazed at the centuries-old superstitions we use,' grinned Jack. 'Modern man! We're still pagans!'

'Superstitions like what?' cried Jackie, who considered himself a very modern young man.

'Like carrying horseshoes for luck, like giving flowers to the bride – they originally symbolised fertility and sexuality; like selecting a particular day or time of the year to ensure good luck and doing all those things we've just mentioned.'

Jackie grinned. 'We just do 'em because they've always been done.'

'But you wouldn't dare stop them!' said Jack.

'They give meaning to the wedding ceremony,' said Caroline Bates. 'Now, Jack, has Grandad mentioned the best days for weddings?'

'He's gone to town on that topic!' he said. 'You'll know some of these verses, and maybe not the others. Now, here's one: "Marry in May, rue for aye". That means it's bad luck to marry in May, summat the human race has believed for over 2,000 years, and he also says: "Marry in Lent, live to

repent". Marriage in Lent was always frowned on, and still is, just as it is not thought wise to marry during other religious times such as Maundy Thursday (which is, in fact, in Lent), St Swithin's Day or Holy Innocents' Day, otherwise known as Childermas. Easter Sunday, when Lent is over and when lots of our old fertility rites are re-enacted by twentieth-century man, is still a favourite time for weddings.'

Caroline nodded in recognition of these ideas, then added, 'But aren't some days and months better than others for weddings?'

'Sure. This is one old verse,' and Jack read it out of Grandad's notebook which he picked up from the sideboard.

> Monday for wealth,
> Tuesday for health,
> Wednesday the best day of all.
> Thursday for losses
> Friday for crosses
> And Saturday no luck at all.'

'Friday is an unlucky day for a lot of things,' said Caroline, 'but in some places, those words are different.'

'You'll always get local variations,' Jack agreed. 'In some places, Wednesday was thought an unlucky day for a wedding, although most agree that Mondays and Tuesdays are lucky and Thursdays and Fridays are not. It's similar to the verse about being born on particular days. The odd thing is that Saturday is reckoned to be unlucky for weddings, although most are celebrated on that day.'

'And months which are lucky? What about those?' asked Caroline.

'Grandad's got a long verse about those,' Jack said. 'June seems the luckiest – that's because it is named after Juno, the faithful and much-loved wife of Jupiter.'

'What was special about her?' grinned Jackie.

'She was the protector of all women,' said

Jack. 'And was the protector of marriage, and it was thought she blessed all those who married during her special month.'

'And that's when the sun's more likely to shine on a bride,' chipped in Annie.

'Right,' said Jack. 'This is the verse Grandad's found and included in his book:

Married in January's hoar and rime
Widowed you'll be before your prime;
Married in February's sleepy weather,
Life you'll tread in time together.
Married when March winds shrill and roar,
Your home will be on a distant shore.
Married under April's changing skies
A chequered path before you lies.
Married when bees over May blossoms flit,
Strangers around your board will sit.
Married in the month of roses – June
Life will be a long honeymoon.
Married in July, with flowers ablaze
Bittersweet memories on after days.
Married in August's heat and drowse
Lover and friend in your chosen spouse
Married in September's golden glow
Smooth and serene your life will go.
Married when leaves in October thin
Toil and hardship for you gain.
Married in veils of November mist
Fortune your wedding ring has kissed.
Married in days of December cheer
Love's star shines brighter from year to year.'

'Fascinating stuff,' yawned Jackie. 'But, well, me and Kathy must be getting to bed...'

'There's one verse before you go,' said Caroline. 'I heard it from my own grandmother, and it adds to Kathy's luck:

Change your name and not the letter
You change for worse and not for better.

'So Kathy's surname might have changed to Merrick, but because the first letter's changed, she's heading for good luck.'

'And there was one very strange custom here in Yorkshire,' added Annie. 'I've not known of it being done for years, but when a bride left her parents' home on the way to be married, someone had to pour boiling water over the doorstep of her old home. They said that before the water dried, someone else in the family would decide to get married! I think that custom has died out now.'

Jackie was now standing up and yawning loudly in his pretence of being tired, but Jack, out of sheer devilment, was not going to let him go yet.

'Grandad's got some notes about wedding rings, an' all, Jackie,' he said, turning the pages of the book. 'He says the wedding ring represents eternity, and that is why it is such an important symbol at a wedding. It unites man and wife. And he reckons the ancients believed that there was a special vein in the fourth finger of the left hand which led directly to the heart, so this made that finger the ideal one for wearing a wedding ring. We still follow that idea.'

'And,' chipped in Annie, 'it was always unlucky if anybody dropped the wedding ring at the ceremony; the priest should pick it up if good luck were to continue. And if a wife lost the ring, her husband should buy another straight away and put in on to her finger without a moment's delay.'

'Ma,' said Caroline, as Jackie launched another loud yawn, 'can you remember when it was customary to have a little love verse engraved inside a wedding ring? My mother had one inside hers – it said "Of all the rest, I love thee best" and I had an aunt whose ring contained a line "In thee my choice I do rejoice".'

'Yes, when I got married, the jeweller offered us a choice of verses which we could have engraved. He had dozens printed on a little card. The one I chose was "God did decree our unity".'

Alan Turner

'Well, I think we'll be off now,' Jackie tried again to leave the room, pulling Kathy to her feet by taking her hand.

Jack smiled and said, 'A wedding, a woo, a clog and a shoe, A pot full o' porridge and away they go!'

'What's that mean?' asked Jackie.

'Dunno,' admitted Jack. 'When children saw a wedding party in the street, they'd take off their shoes or clogs and throw them after the party. Now I might just take off my shoes and throw them after you two if you hang about here much longer!'

'Right, that's good enough for us, come on, Kathy. Goodnight all.'

'Goodnight,' they chorused as the happy couple left, 'and thanks for the supper.'

When they'd gone, Caroline Bates indicated the notebook and said, 'Jack, long before NY closed down, and before Sam died, Alan Turner was making some notes for Sam's book. He asked me to type them up when I was NY Estates secretary; apparently, your Grandad had seen Alan in the Wool-

pack, and had mentioned this idea to him, so Alan had put some ideas on paper. I just wondered if he'd ever given them to Grandad.'

'Aye, I think he had. Alan's keen on conserving things to be seen in the countryside, isn't he? Like market crosses, fairs and dovecotes, and he's interested in the way we name things like fields, hills, rivers and so on.'

At this point, Annie decided to go upstairs to bed, leaving Jack with Caroline Bates. They bade her goodnight and Jack poured them another drink each.

'Right, let's see what Alan Turner has sent in.' Jack joined Caroline on the settee and opened Grandad's notes.

'Here we are, in your fair hand – well, your fair typewritten notes!' smiled Jack. 'His first piece is about market crosses.'

MARKET CROSSES

'Yorkshire has some fine market crosses, but because some look like castles and many are buildings with roofs, walls and even staircases, we tend to forget that they really are market crosses. At Beverley, in East Yorkshire, for example, the market cross was erected in the eighteenth century, and this one is an open shelter with stone pillars supporting a cupola roof. It is decorated with stone urns, the Royal Arms of England and France, and the arms of Beverley town, which depicts a beaver over a lake.

'There's another splendid one down south, in Chichester in fact; built in 1501 for "the comfort of the poore people" who came to sell their wares in the town, it is an octagonal structure with seats inside and clock faces above. It was once used as an ecclesiastical court, when the punished had to wear a white sheet, and it has always been a focal point for market trading.

'These are just two examples of splendid crosses, but most are simply stone pillars with a cross on the top, some of which are surrounded by steps. As the name implies, these are generally located in the market places of country towns and villages, although lots have been demolished, either deliberately or by accident, and some have been transferred away from their original site.

'In medieval times, it was the custom to erect a tall stone cross in the market place to add a touch of solemnity. It was felt that any business conducted under the sign of the cross must benefit from this closeness to religion, and that the presence of this symbol of faith would encourage honesty and fair play.

'The crosses therefore became a focal point for community matters – announcements were made from their steps, they were the centre of many assemblies and events from prayer meetings to rent collections, mystery plays were held in front of them and, of course, the market traders used them as a centrepiece. At Ripon in Yorkshire, the Major was elected before the market cross and wandering monks would halt there for prayers during their journeyings. And it is a fair bet that many courtships have been cemented through meetings beneath the market crosses of this land.

'With the British weather, many of these events would be hampered by rain or snow and so it made sense to erect roofs over the crosses. In this way, the gatherings were kept safe from our inclement weather, but this encouraged some townsfolk to try and outclass their neighbours by building bigger and better crosses. As they assumed greater importance, so they became even more splendid until some had offices, meeting rooms, spires and ornate steps leading into the upper chambers. But they were still called market crosses.

'It was then decided in some towns to have a smaller cross for particular goods

which were on sale, and so in some markets, such as Shaftesbury, there were Fish Crosses, Butter Crosses and Cheese Crosses, while at Bridgwater in Somerset there was a Pig Cross.

'It is pleasing to note that it's hoped to replace market crosses which have been lost or removed; at Selby in Yorkshire the cross was moved from the market place to Selby Park because it had become a traffic hazard, but some residents feel it should be returned. At Stokesley, in North Yorkshire, the market cross was damaged in 1746 when rioting youths lit a fire around it, and again in 1779 when a celebratory fire cracked it so badly that it had to be dismantled. A new one is needed.

'It would be so nice to see a traditional stone cross in every market place in Britain.'

ON DOVECOTES

Turner's contribution to Grandad's notes continued with:

'Throughout the ages doves have been associated with religions of all kinds, usually depicting purity and peace, and in the Christian faith they are said to be the emblem of the Holy Ghost. When it was thought that a witch could turn herself into an animal or bird, this did not include a dove. Doves were beyond the reach of evil in whatever form.

'It is not surprising that the people therefore built substantial homes for these birds, although in the Middle Ages there was also a very practical reason for constructing spacious and impressive dovecotes.

'Dovecotes are simply homes for doves. They live, nest and sleep within them, and they can be found in the grounds of many of our stately homes, in or around farms, or even created from cracks in cliffs and crags, and they vary in size from those which will accommodate a few dozen birds up to those which will house hundreds or even thousands. Some are made of wood, some are built of stone or brick and some are even hollowed out of a hillside. Yet more are built within churches – one example is at Selby Abbey in North Yorkshire; high in the galleries above the nave area, the walls are peppered with small round holes. These once contained short wooden perches for use by the doves which lived in the tower.

'Another one near a church was created for 600 birds by the Knights Hospitallers in medieval times and is at Garway between Hereford and Monmouth; the National Trust shows two interesting half-timbered dovecotes at Hawford and Wichenford, both near Worcester. There is another noteworthy one at Bamburgh in Northumberland which was built between 1400 and 1500. It is made of stone and is a conical shape; it will accommodate 250 birds, while one at Penmon on the isle of Anglesey was built around 1600 for over a thousand birds. I'm sure there are others.

'In the early days of our history, only a

Lord of the Manor was allowed to possess a dovecote and at this time, they were a matter of practicability. Because guns had not been invented and because doves were a good source of food, especially since they reproduced themselves so well, it was convenient that doves could be encouraged to live in little cottages; the word cot means cottage. There they could nest and breed in comfort and safety, and His Lordship could also catch those he required for the table. The young were called squabs, and it was these which made such excellent pies; consequently, the dovecote was a very useful means of providing food, especially during the winter when hunting was often far from easy.

'For the poor peasants, however, this situation was far from welcome. His Lordship's doves often raided their crops and the unfortunate peasants were not allowed to kill them, an offence which carried imprisonment or even death.

'There is a superstition that it is unlucky to destroy a dovecote, and this might well be the source of it!

'Gradually, those restrictions were lifted and the sixteenth, seventeenth and nineteenth centuries witnessed a spate of dovecote building. Many are now considered worthy of preservation as buildings of special architectural interest.

'One of the oldest surviving superstitions about doves is that a person cannot die when lying on a pillow stuffed with the feathers of a dove. This probably comes from this bird's links with the Holy Ghost, the idea being that the Holy Ghost is eternal, and so a pillow of another kind was given to the sufferer so that a peaceful death would follow. If it was necessary to prolong the life so that a will could be drawn up or if relatives were travelling from a distance, then the dove feathered pillow was left in position! Taking it away was known as Drawing the Pillow.

'Doves, like most birds, are said to forecast the weather and there is a saying that doves always wash before rain, and that they will come home slowly to their dovecote in the evening if the weather is to be wet.'

FAIRS

Alan Turner's note said, 'There are so many fairs in Britain that it is not possible to discuss them all, but it is necessary to persuade people not to use that silly, artificial word *fayre* which has no basis in reality!

'The word comes from feire or feriae which means a saint's day or a holy day, from which we get our "holiday", and the original fairs were very business-like institutions designed to be a focus of trading in livestock and other goods. Any surviving horse fairs are good examples of this. The fun side came later, and as markets took over the commercial aspect, some fairs became purely for entertainment. Many modern fairs comprise nothing but amusements and sideshows.

'Those early fairs could not be held without a royal charter and many of these remain effective; the charters specified the dates and duration of each fair, and allowed the Lord of the Manor to establish the fair. He could, however, let certain other rights to different people – for example, someone might supply all the booths at a small cost.

'A later type of fair, which was not one of those ancient charter fairs, emerged in Elizabethan times. The law said that meetings must be held at certain times of the year to determine the wages of those in domestic or farm service, and to allow farm hands, domestic workers and servants to assemble and seek work. The employers could meet prospective employees to talk about their terms and the merits of working for a particular person. These Hiring Fairs sometimes lasted a week and formed the annual, and only, holiday for the workers. Entertainments, competitions of skill, dancing, music, drink and food were all part of the fun, and when it was all over, they returned to work for the rest of the year until the next Hiring Fair.

'In most parts of the country, these Hiring Fairs (sometimes just called Hirings) were usually held at Martinmas; in some areas, they were called Mop Fairs because those seeking work would wear a small badge to denote the work they could do. Potential shepherds wore a piece of sheepswool, waggoners carried whips, milkmaids a piece of cowhair and those seeking domestic work carried a mop!

'When a worker was hired in Yorkshire, the agreement was sealed by the employer handing to the employee a coin called the fastning penny. This could be of any value – in the very early days it was probably one penny, but later it became a shilling, a florin, a half-crown or even a crown. This could be spent during the Hiring Fair, but it was knocked off the wages at the end of the year – and a year's wages a century ago might be no more than £14 a year for a ploughlad, or £15 per year for a domestic servant. A worker wishing to end the contract with an employer could do so by handing back the fastning penny, sometimes known as God's Penny. Hiring Fairs ended when the Agricultural Wages Act was passed in 1924.

'One odd aspect of these occurs in the north; the Martinmas Hiring Fairs were on the Feast of St Martin, which is November 11th. But in the north, they were held on November 23rd, the old Martinmas Day. The change to the Gregorian calendar abolished ten days but the canny Yorkshire farmers refused to pay their men for those missing days.

'Even now, many of them think that Martinmas is on November 23rd, the time it would have been held if Pope Gregory had not changed the calendar.

'Here in Yorkshire, there are efforts to revive some of our ancient fairs, such as Scarborough Fair, which was first held in 1253, the Lammastide Fair at York and Masham Sheep Fair.'

LOOKING AT NAMES

Alan Turner's contribution continued with a few notes about the naming of features of the landscape like fields, hills and rivers.

Fields

'The names of the fields surrounding any village can provide marvellous clues to its history and can involve some fascinating research among parish records, old books and maps. Most of the names have come to us through past generations of farmers who have used this method of describing their land because it is a simple means of identification. We continue to use it although modern farmers probably change the older names to suit their present purposes.

'Some are very obvious – such as Ten Acre, Hundred Acre, Beckside, Moor End, Nine Furlong, Foxglade, Woodside and so forth – while others do need a little imagination to understand their sources – for example, Maypole Hill, Canal Bottoms, Witch Carrs, Croft Ings, Hob Acres, Lower Leyes, Crag Top Intake and so on.

'Some of the names in that list therefore require a little explanation: a carr, or The Carrs, refers to an area of heavy, rough, marshy ground which is not close to the moors. It is usually low-lying. Ings is another word for a pasture which is wet and low-lying, and many boggy ings are covered with water and have become havens for wild life. A ley generally refers to a rich arable field which has been put down to grass while in Yorkshire, an intake, or intak as it is often called, refers to an enclosure which has been reclaimed from the moors. A glade is an open space between trees while a slack is a hollow in the landscape, such as Moss Slack or Hazel Slack.

'Folklore comes into names too, such as Witch Carrs and Hob Acres; a hob was an elf or shaggy-haired dwarf who lived in the outbuildings of old farms and secretly helped with the work, so long as he liked the farmer's family and they kept him fed with cream. There are names of locations like Hob Garth, Hob Dale, Hob Green and Hob Moor to remind us of these fairy creatures, and on the Moors there is a place called Fairy Cross Plain.

'One very common name in Yorkshire is Lousey, which can be found in Lousey Carr, Lousey Lane, Lousey Leys and similar names, although it has been corrupted into Lucy in some cases. This can be spelt as Loosey but it is nothing to do with a girl called Lucy, or with lice! It comes from an old word meaning pig-sty and so Lucy Carrs, Lousey Lanes and so forth were once places where pigs were kept or where they roamed.

'There is an old word "neukin" which means a corner and this sometimes appears in field names as nook. Another Yorkshire word is "rake" – this refers to a place where sheep could wander and be pastured on a right of stray, and is reflected in names like Rakeside or Rake Farm. Names like garths, closes, crofts, flatts have all come to us from either the Anglo-Saxons, the Vikings, Normans and others who have invaded us and worked our land, while history is revealed in Battle Field, Monk's Pasture, King's Meadow and so forth.

'There is an old saying that "Fields have eyes, but woods have ears" and that's worth remembering when you are walking or picnicking in someone's field!

Hills

'In Yorkshire and other parts of the north of England we refer to our valleys as dales and there are literally hundreds of dales in Yorkshire, some very tiny and others covering a huge area. But we give our hills different names. Over to the west, in the Pennine region, we call them fells. This can mean a mountain, as in the Lake District where it appears in names like Scafell or the tough sport of fell racing, but it can also mean the slope of a mountain or a piece of elevated open moorland – in the Yorkshire Dales, it usually means the latter. "Fell" may come from an Old English word meaning "measure of land". This word does not seem to be used on the eastern side of Yorkshire where the uplands are known as moors.

'The word moor means an open, uncultivated stretch of land. It used to include commons too, but now it usually refers to high land covered with heather. Within the North York Moors National Park and the Yorkshire Dales National Park there are many moors with their own distinctive names.

'Another name for hills is wolds. This also means uncultivated uplands and the Yorkshire Wolds were once described as an open, sandy, barren, extensive sheepwalk! Now, they are a lush panorama of greenery and beautifully cultivated farmlands. There are other wolds, including those in Lincolnshire and, of course, the word appears in the Cotswolds.

'Yorkshire folk have other names for hills, like banks, ridges, riggs, nabs, howes and barughs (pronounced barfs), while a few are called toppings. The word pen also means a hill, and this is evident in Pennines and also names like Penyghent and Pendle, both hills in the Pennine range.

Rivers

'Yorkshire rivers and streams have various names, such as gills, becks, spouts, burns and fosses. A river is generally the largest flow of water, with streams, becks or burns flowing into it. Gills are tiny watercourses, often in a deep valley or ravine, while fosses and spouts are generally waterfalls on smaller waterways. You can see how Beckindale got its name – a beck or small stream in a valley or dale!'

CHAPTER ELEVEN

ON TYKES,
TOWNS AND TREES

*He goes not out of his way that goes
to a fine inn.*

Sam Pearson's notebook

The Woolpack was empty; Joe Sugden had called for a swift half but Amos leaned across the bar to ask, 'And what have you contributed to your Grandad's notebook, Joe?'

'Nowt, Amos. I was in France for some of the time he was working on it, and before that he reckoned I was too young to know owt about folklore.'

'But you'll be making some contribution?' There was a slightly shocked tone to Amos' voice.

'Aye, I will, so you needn't think I've opted out! I've made a few notes and I'll give 'em to our Jack shortly.'

'Not French lore, I trust!' chuckled Amos. 'That'd upset folks hereabouts.'

'I did pick up some French lore, Amos. They're just like us when it comes to worrying about the weather. How about:

If the weather is fine, put on your coat;
If it's wet, do as you please.

'That's like the Scottish idea that a wise man should carry his coat in dry weather, and a fool needs his when it rains.'

'Aye, well, that's mebbe not so bad,' Amos agreed.

'And,' smiled Joe, 'in France, they say that women and fortune change like the weather. Then in the Loire valley where the wine comes from, it's said that "a rainy year makes the fruit very dear".'

'Aye, well…'

Joe interrupted Amos as he went on, 'They also say that "a frost year is a good year for wheat and for fruit, and a year of snow is a year of plenty"; they're sensible, French sayings, Amos.'

'Very like ours, if I may say so,' Amos declared.

'There's similar sayings in Spain, Portugal, Italy and elsewhere,' Joe said. 'When we say "Rain before seven, fine before eleven", the French say "Morning rains are soon past"

and the Chinese agree by saying "When it rains about the break of day, the traveller's sorrows soon pass away".'

'Aye, well, I can't say as I've seen many Chinamen in Beckindale. But the French, they'll have sayings about the wine harvest, I suppose?'

'Like "Hoar frost is good for vines, but bad for corn", eh?' grinned Joe. 'Or "Comets are said to improve the wine crop". Did you know, Amos, that if lots of comets appear during the year, the French refer to that year's wines as comet wines?'

'Nay, now I can't say as I did know that, Joe. But I can't see that Sam's notebook wants lore from foreign parts.'

'You're dead right, Amos. So I've made lists of odds and ends that I thought the others might leave out, things to get people talking, especially here in the Woolpack.'

Amos' eyes brightened at the thought. 'Now that's a good idea, Joe, to get 'em arguing, discussing, using their brains and digging deep for knowledge of the past. So what have you come up with?'

Joe pulled a small red notebook from his pocket and said, 'It's all in here, Amos. Sam Pearson's grandson's notebook. Right, let's see what I turn up first.'

YORKSHIRE TYKES

Joe opened the book at notes about Yorkshire tykes.

'Now, Amos, why are Yorkshiremen called tykes?'

'Nay, Joe, that's summat as I've never heard explained. I would guess it's because we're fine upstanding folk.'

'Right, now listen. First, I think it refers only to men and second, it's not very complimentary. Leastways, it wasn't in the first instance, but mebbe it now is. Anyroad, Amos, the word probably comes from the Old Norse tongue, so it is part of our dialect heritage, but originally it meant a dog or a

Joe Sugden

cur, and it came to mean a rough, uncultured and ill-mannered fellow.'

'Then it doesn't apply these days,' countered Amos, "cos modern Yorkshiremen are charming, cultured, polite and very socially acceptable. Like us Brearlys, really.'

'That could be true, Amos!' grinned Joe. 'Now, the term Yorkshire tyke came to mean a country man from Yorkshire, but only from the West Riding. North Riding and East Riding men weren't tykes.'

'Us Brearlys have strong connections with Bridlington in East Yorkshire,' Amos said. 'Good stock, tha knows.'

Joe continued, 'But folks who had no idea of the size of Yorkshire referred to all Yorkshiremen as tykes, and so the name has stuck. Once, it meant only sporting types – hunting, shooting and fishing folk – then it gradually came to mean us all. But,' he emphasised with a smile, 'there's some good news because a tike, spelt with an "i", was a dog of the terrier breed. And it was a very good dog indeed, totally sound, good at

ratting and catching vermin, ready to tackle a cat at any time or even a fox, badger or rat. Tikes were ideal dogs for poachers, Amos, and became known as sneck dogs – that's dogs that will sneck, or catch, anything.

'In the old days, there were songs about Yorkshire tykes, like "A Wonder, or an Honest Yorkshireman" which was sung around 1736, and which had a line "If thoo can trust a Yorkshire tyke, a rogue thoo'll never find me". Another song, called "The Yorkshire Horsedealers", sung around 1850, had a line which went, "Hard by Clapham town-end, lived an awd Yorkshire tyke…" That's Clapham in the Dales, not the London Clapham.'

'I never knew there was a Clapham down south,' said Amos.

'Anyway,' Joe said, 'a tyke could mean a dog, an unruly, rough fellow, a country youth from West Yorkshire, a low, churlish person, a mean, disreputable man or a country lad.'

'Or a fine terrier good at sniffing out vermin!' beamed Amos.

'Or a clownish rustic, an old horse or a wide-awake Yorkshireman who might turn to dishonesty!' said Joe. 'There's one old saying which goes "Shake a bridle over a Yorkshireman's grave, and he'll rise and steal a horse". But I reckon a tyke is now a fine, upstanding fellow of immense character and style.'

'Just like us Brearlys,' added Amos.

'Right, now one thing the tykes of West Yorkshire did, years ago, was to introduce the two West Riding Commandments and they are:

1. Cop hod an' stick
That means hold on to what you've got:
2. Hear all, see all, say nowt
Eat all, drink all, pay nowt
And if thoo ivver does owt for nowt
Do it for thyself
That needs no explanation!'

'Then there's the Yorkshireman's coat of arms,' added Amos. 'It's a fly, a flea, a magpie and a flitch of bacon. Now, you see, Joe, a fly will have a drink with anybody, and so will a Yorkshireman; a flea will bite anybody, and so will a Yorkshireman; a magpie will chatter with anybody, and so will a Yorkshireman, and a flitch of bacon is no good until it's been hanged, and neither is a Yorkshireman!'

'It's a good job we can laugh at ourselves, Amos. Now, there's the Yorkshireman's toast – "Here's to us, all of us, and me and all, May we never want anything, none of us, nor me neither".'

'And the Yorkshireman's anthem, Joe. Ikley Moor baht 'at. That means Ilkley Moor without a hat.'

'I've got a note of the words, Amos, just in case you ever find a Yorkshireman who doesn't know them. They go like this:

Where hast tha been since I saw thee?
On Ilkley Moor baht 'at.
Tha's been acourting Mary Jane,
On Ilkley Moor baht 'at.
Tha's going to catch a death o' cawd
On Ilkley Moor baht 'at.
Then we shall have to bury thee,
On Ilkley Moor baht 'at,
Then t'worms'll come and eat thee up,
On Ilkley Moor baht 'at
Then t'ducks'll come and eat up t'worms,
On Ilkley Moor baht 'at.
Then we shall come and eat up t'ducks
On Ilkley Moor baht 'at.
Then we shall all have etten thee
On Ilkley Moor baht 'at.'

'A song that's sung in the very best hostelries,' smiled Amos, 'especially after the best of Yorkshire ales.'

FARMERS' SAYINGS

'Right,' said Joe, 'that's a few things about Yorkshiremen, so now for a few about farmers. Do you know the Farmer's Toast and the Farmer's Lament?'

'Nay, I don't.' Amos broke off to serve a customer.

'Right, this is the toast:

Let the wealthy and great
Roll in splendour and state –
I envy them not, I declare it.
I eat my own lamb
My chickens and ham
I shear my own fleece and I wear it.
I have lawns, I have bowers,
I have fruit, I have flowers,
The lark is my morning's alarmer.

So joyfully boys now
Here's God speed the plough,
Long life and success to the farmer.'

'And the lament?' asked Amos.

'I'll give the Yorkshire farmer's lament,'
said Joe. 'It was written in dialect in 1860 by a
farmer from Oswaldkirk – that's a village
near Helmsley in Ryedale – so I'm repeating
it in the exact words of the time:

It rains ageean, Ah deea declare,
It's two days wet for yar day fair;
Syke times as these was nivver seen
Us farmers'll be beggared clean.

Crops is seea bad ah's verra flade
Rents, rates, tares'll not get paid.
Harvest folks' wages ganning on
And there they stand, can't deea a ton.

What a sad mess of mouldy hay
And taties rotting all away,
Wheat thin on t'grund an' small at ear
It can't yield wheel, ah's verra seer.

Wots'll be leet, seea leet ah say
At t'better horf'll blaw away;
Beeans hez neea swods, they've nowt but
top
And t'barley isn't horf a crop.

Fog dissn't grow as wheel as owt
And t'tonnups'll be good for nowt;
Pastures is nobbut verra bare
And stock comes down at ivvery fair.

There's nowt to eeat for t'milking kye
And meeast on 'em'll soon be dry;

Times noo for farmers is seea bad
You'll see next spring they'll breeak like
mad.'

Amos frowned, 'Folks'll not understand
those words, Joe.'

'Then they'll have to fathom 'em out
somehow, Amos, get their thinking caps on,
as we say. I'll give a clue or two – flade is
afraid, wots are oats, swods are pods, fog is

the grass in a meadow after the hay harvest,
tonnups are turnips and kye are cows.'

'Aye, well, thanks for that. I trust you've
summat that's a bit easier for my customers
to understand.'

'How about animals, Amos? There's a
verse about their ages; in fact, there are
several verses about this. Here's two:

Thrice the age of a dog is that of a horse;
Thrice the age of a horse is that of a man;
Thrice the age of a man is that of a deer;
Thrice the age of a deer is that of an eagle.

'The next one is ideal for people in your
profession, Amos, because it goes:

The horse and mule live thirty years
And nothing know of wines or beers;
The goat and sheep, they also die
And never taste of Scotch or rye;
The cow drinks water by the ton
And at eighteen years is almost done;
Without the aid of rum or gin
The dog at fifteen cashes in;
The cat in milk and water soaks
But then in twelve short years it croaks;
The modest, sober, bone-dry hen
Lays eggs for nogs and dies at ten;
All animals that are strictly dry
Live sinless lives and quickly die.
But sinful, ginful, rum-soaked man
Survives for three score years and ten;
And some of us, a mighty few
Keep drinking till we're ninety-two.'

Amos smiled. 'Can you let me have
copies of these, Joe, and I'll have some fun in
the pub, getting folks to remember them.'

ANIMAL NOISES

'And what about the sounds of animals,
Amos? Try our customers with: the drone of
bees; the hum of insects; the boom of
bitterns; the whistle of thrushes; the crowing
of cocks; the cooing of doves; the bleating of
lambs; the quacking of ducks; the honking

of geese; the chirping of crickets and
grasshoppers; the grunting of pigs; the
chatter of magpies; the screech of owls; the
buzz of flies; the bellow of stags; the call of
foxes; the chirping of sparrows; the twitter-
ing of swallows; the gobble of turkeys; the
drumming of the snipe; the laughing of
woodpeckers; the screaming of peacocks;
the braying of donkeys; the mooing of cows
and neighing of horses. There must be more,
Amos.'

'Now that lot might give my customers
summat to think about, Joe. And there's the
mutter of customers!' he smiled.

TOWN

'Another thing that's worthy of discussion,
Amos,' said Joe, 'is the range of rhymes
about places in Yorkshire. Some aren't very
complimentary, but they'll certainly get a
lively discussion under way. How about this
for starters:

> Bradford for cash, Halifax for dash,
> Wakefield for pride and poverty;
> Huddersfield for show, Sheffield's what's
>   low
> Leeds for dirt and vulgarity!'

'Now a landlord has to be careful not to
upset his regulars, Joe. I'm not sure I dare
produce that' un.'

'All right, how about:

> Birstall for ringers, Heckmondwike for
>   singers,
> Dewsbury for pedlars, Cleckheaton for
>   sheddlers.

> Bedale bonnets and Bedale faces
> There's nowt to beat 'em in any places.

> Castleford lasses may well be fair
> They wash in t'Calder and rinse in t'Aire.

> Hutton Rudby and Enterpen
> Far more rogues than honest men.

> Marrick church is seen the best
> Just as the sun has gone to rest.

Hodder, Calder, Ribble and rain
Mingle together in Mitton domain.

Skipton in Craven is never a haven
But many a day of foul weather,
And he that would say, to a pretty girl nay
I wish for his cravat a tether.

Selby was a seaport town
When Goole was nobbut a marsh;
Now Goole it is a seaport town
And it's Selby that fares the worse.

Said the Devil when flying over Harrogate
    wells,
I think I'm getting near home by the
    smells!

Halifax is built o' wax; Heptonstall o'
    stooan
In Halifax, there's bonny lasses
In Hepstonstall, there's none.'

Joe smiled at Amos, who was struggling to memorise at least one or two verses, and said, 'Don't worry, Amos, I'll see you get a copy of all these. Now, what about sayings like "From Hell, Hull and Halifax, Good Lord deliver us", and the famous one about the Scarborough warning – it goes:

The Scarborough warning –
A word and a blow,
But the blow comes first.

'How did these originate?' Joe continued. 'A very good question, Joe. You'll send me a copy of summat about those, an' all?'

'I will, but first an explanation. Now the Hell, Hull and Halifax saying. In the seventeenth and eighteenth centuries, Yorkshire was the busiest area outside London for making counterfeit coins.'

'I did read about that in a local book,' said Amos.

'Right, and the busiest towns in Yorkshire were Hull and Halifax. They had more coiners than any of the other places, but the punishments in those towns were notorious. Halifax had the infamous Halifax Gibbet, which was in fact a horse-operated guillotine. It was being used long before the guillotine became so popular in France; a horse was harnessed to a rope which hauled up the blade. The coiners had to place their heads on the block, the rope was cut and down came the blade. Now the Halifax Gibbet was in use during the reign of Edward III (1327–1377) when execution days were Tuesdays, Thursdays and Saturdays, the victims being despatched on the first market day following their conviction. The Halifax Gibbet was last used in April 1650. In France a similar machine, designed by Joseph Ignace Guillotin, was first used, after extensive testing, on 25th April 1792. It executed a thief called Nicolas-Jacques Pelletier. The Halifax coiners knew that if they were caught, they would lose their heads on this machine. In Hull, however, coiners were executed below the high-water mark by being hanged on a conventional gibbet, this curious location being within the jurisdiction of the Admiralty. As the coiners feared both towns, it led to them saying "From Hell, Hull and Halifax, Good Lord deliver us".'

'Makes you shudder, doesn't it?' Amos gave an involuntary shiver as he thought about Joe's words. 'And the Scarborough warning? What was that?'

'Well, that means no warning at all,' Joe told him. 'One story, which is often told but might not be the true origin of the Scarborough warning, concerns a raid on Scarborough Castle in 1557. The castle was supposed to be impregnable but Thomas, the second son of Lord Stafford, disguised his troops as peasants and on a market day, when the town was busy with strangers, he and his men simply walked into the castle through the main gates and gained control. He achieved this without bloodshed and without the townspeople even knowing.

Hence the saying that a Scarborough warning is no warning at all. Stafford's success was short-lived; three days later, the Earl of Westmorland regained the castle for the King and Stafford was executed. But there is a belief that the term Scarborough warning was in use before this raid. There is a reference to it in John Heywood's *Proverbs* (1546); he repeats it in 1562 in his *Epigrams upon Proverbs*, while in 1589 George Puttenham defines it as "Skarborow warning, for a sodaine commandement, allowing no respect or delay to bethinke a man of his business".'

Another customer now entered and Amos went to serve him, so Joe drained his glass and said. 'Well, I must be off, Amos.'

'Send me copies of these items, Joe.'

'I will, and some more. See you,' and Joe left the Woolpack.

LOGS

In the comfort of his home Joe looked through his own notes, deciding which he should copy for Amos. He felt the regulars of the Woolpack might be interested in which logs made the best fires, along with his collected notes about Yule logs. He'd make sure that Jack was given these for inclusion in Grandad's book to complement any general notes about trees. He paused at a page where he had written a verse:

Oaken logs if dry and old
Keep away the winter's cold;
Poplar gives a bitter smoke
Fills your eyes and makes you choke;
Elm wood burns like graveyard mould,
Even the very flames are cold;
Apple wood will scent the room
Pear wood smells as flowers in bloom;
But ash wood wet and ash wood dry
A King to warm his slippers by.
Beech wood fires burn bright and clear
If the logs are kept for a year;

Chestnut's only good, they say,
If for years, 'tis stored away.
Birch and firwoods burn too fast
Blaze too bright, and do not last;
But ash wood green and ash wood brown
Are fit for a Queen with a golden crown.

Joe found some notes which said that other woods had merits, such as the hornbeam which blazed nicely if it had been kept for a year, while logs from firs and pines did provide a welcome blaze but tended to spit out sparks. Yew is good for burning because it makes a warm blaze, and holly should be burnt when it is green. In common with other fruit trees, cherry logs give the room a lovely scent but the alder, like the elm is a very bad burner.

THE YULE LOG

One customary log to be burnt every year is the Yule Log, and Joe could recall his Grandad's insistence upon this practice every Christmas. Some country folk would select their Yule Log as early as Candlemas Day (February 2), and then store it so that it would be dry for the following Christmas Eve. The type of timber was not too important, although some liked the wood of fruit trees because of the lovely scents they produced when burning, while others liked the hawthorn which blazed so warmly, or the oak which lasted a long time. The only general rule was that the log be a large one. In these modern times, small fireplaces cannot cope with a log that is too big, but many farms acquired a Yule Log about four feet long (just over one metre), and hauled it to the house with a lot of noise and fuss, sometimes accompanied by singing and drinking. In France, Joe knew, the youngest of the family poured wine over it and hymns would be sung before the log was committed to the fire.

Wherever the custom is practised, the

Sayings about trees

He that loveth a tree, loveth a branch.
You cannot judge a tree by its bark.
He who plants a walnut tree should not expect to see its fruit.
A forest takes a long time to grow, but can be reduced to ashes in minutes.
Little strokes can fell great oaks.
Great oaks from little acorns grow.
It is always cold when the blackthorn is in flower.
The willow is weak, but it serves to bind stronger wood.

Yule Log is lit on Christmas Eve and it should be done by burning the remains of the previous year's log. These small, charred remnants are usually kept under a bed (where some believe they ward off lightning strikes). As the old log is placed on the fire, the new log is ignited from it and it should be allowed to smoulder throughout the Christmas period until Twelfth Night. The remains are kept under the bed, or in a dry outbuilding, until the following Christmas when the whole procedure starts again.

It was thought unlucky if the Yule Log fire went out, and in some areas it was believed that if a young girl touched the log before washing her hands, the fire would burn dully; another idea was that the prettiest girl in the room should sit on the log before it was placed in the fire, and then a toast should be drunk by everyone else. This was thought to date to the times when human sacrifices were cast upon the pagans' huge Yuletide bonfires fuelled by Yule logs, which added light to the Winter Solstice.

Joe made a note to remind Amos to secure a Yule Log for the Woolpack's bar fire at Christmas time.

TREES

While Joe was deciding which portions to give to Amos, Jack was examining Grandad's book and came across the section dealing with trees. There were some old superstitions, such as that garlands of birch hung on a wall will keep away evil spirits, while the wood of the rowan (mountain ash) should be used for making beams over the fireplace, to keep away witches.

Other rural beliefs were that if a beech was felled for timber, it should be done before Midsummer Day because the wood would then last three times as long.

Various trees were thought to protect the house against witches and evil spirits, and were consequently grown nearby, such as the elder, the rowan, the holly, the hazel and the hawthorn, while others, such as the lilac and the blackthorn, should never be taken indoors as they are omens of death.

WARTS

Meanwhile, back at the Woolpack, customers were filling the bar. Amos had been listening to an argument between some of his regulars, and realised their discussion was an ideal topic for Sam Pearson's notebook. As the men chattered, he made surreptitious notes. The subject was the curing of warts.

At the end of the session, Amos had these suggestions: smear them with the juice of a dandelion flower's stem; collect fresh rainwater on a teasel, and pour it on the warts; rub them with castor oil; apply the juice of the celandine; rub them with the inside of a pod from a broad bean plant and say 'As this pod rots away, so my warts will die'; smear them with the milky substances of the thistle, the marigold or the crowsfoot; touch them all with a separate pea pod then bury the pods so that as they rot, the warts will all disappear.

The cures continued, some suggesting the services of a wart charmer, others a doctor. The best-known cure of all was this: steal a piece of beef, rub it on the warts and bury the beef in the soil. As the beef rots, the warts will go. This is the witch's cure and is recommended by many country folk.

And, as Amos had overheard, the best way to avoid warts is never to put your hands in water that has been used to boil eggs, or which has been used to wash them.

CLAY PIPES

While looking through the notebook, Jack found a piece in Grandad's handwriting referring to clay pipes.

'I think Amos ought to have some genuine clay pipes hanging in the bar of the Woolpack,' Grandad had written. 'In my day, churchwarden pipes, as we called them, were given free by a good landlord to his regular customers. They were very fragile, being made of white clay, and a genuine churchwarden pipe had a long, curved stem. Some smokers did not like these, and so they simply smashed them off at a length to suit themselves. Landlords stored the pipes in racks which catered for long and short stems, and after the evening's drinking was over, a good landlord would collect all the pipes from the smokers and stick the tips of their stems into a fire to purify them.

'Before handing out the pipes next time most landlords would dip the stems into some beer, because this prevented the clay from sticking to the lips of the smokers.

Some regulars insisted on having their personal pipes, but as the cost of beer went up, landlords began to sell the pipes instead of issuing them free of charge.

'Clay pipes have been manufactured in this country since about 1590 and they became popular after Sir Walter Raleigh introduced tobacco some 20 years earlier. Originally, pipes were made from porcelain or even silver, but the humble material of clay made pipes accessible to the ordinary person. Now, here's a story about King James I. He hated smoking, and it is said that the distinctive lump underneath the bowl of a churchwarden pipe represents his bearded face! This decoration sometimes bears the trademark of the maker of the pipe.

'In its early days tobacco was very expensive so the pipes were very small, but exquisitely made and decorated with carvings and symbols. But that bearded lump underneath made it impossible to set the pipes down when upright, and so in time, it became the practice to make pipes with flat bottoms; then as the price of tobacco grew less, so the bowls became larger.

'The name churchwarden was given to these pipes because they were smoked by churchwardens who met to discuss parish affairs, later adjourning to the local inn for refreshment.'

And finally, Sam Pearson had added, 'I hope people find my notes both useful and interesting when I've passed on.'

'Aye,' said Jack quietly to himself. 'They will.'

POSTSCRIPT

Joe called to see Jack one evening at Emmerdale Farm.
'Well, Jack,' he said, 'you've examined Grandad's notebook; what do
you think of it?'
'Interesting,' said Jack. 'Full of stuff that might have got lost
if he hadn't written it down. I'm keen on conversation, as you know,
and that means conservation of folk ideas and customs as
well as the environment.'
'You remember that note Grandad put in? He said he hoped
his grandchildren and others would find it interesting and useful.
I think he wants you to publish it, otherwise why mention
others in the way he did?'
'You reckon?'
'Aye, I do. I think that you, with your knowledge of the
publishing world, could do summat about it, for us all, and for
Grandad especially. Look at it this way, you might decide to move
on somewhere else; in any case, you won't be here for ever and
neither will I, so I think we owe it to Grandad to give it a wider
audience. If we keep it at Emmerdale, it's bound to get lost one
of these days.'
'As a matter of fact,' grinned Jack. 'I do know
a publisher in London who might be interested. I'll have
a word with them . . .'

INDEX